Junior Praise

Compiled by
Phil Burt, Peter Horrobin and Greg Leavers

Combined Words Edition

Marshall Pickering
An Imprint of HarperCollins*Publishers*

Marshall Pickering
An imprint of HarperCollins*Religious*
Part of HarperCollins*Publishers*
77-85 Fulham Palace Road
Hammersmith
London W6 8JB

First published in Great Britain in 1992 by Marshall Pickering

This edition 1997

1 3 5 7 9 10 8 6 4 2

Compilation © 1992 Phil Burt, Peter Horrobin and Greg Leavers

The compilers assert the moral right to be identified as the compilers of this work

A catalogue record for this book is available from the British Library

ISBN 0 551 02638 3

Combined Music Edition ISBN 0 551 04014 9

Text set by Barnes Music Engraving Ltd, East Sussex, England
Printed and bound in Great Britain by Caledonian International Book Manufacturing Ltd, Glasgow

1

A boy gave to Jesus
five loaves and two fish,
not much, you might say, for a crowd;
but Jesus, He took them
and smiled at the lad,
gave thanks to His Father
and blessed them out loud.

The boy then saw Jesus
take loaves and the fish,
not much for the folk on that day;
but Jesus, He broke them
and smiled at the lad,
gave bits to disciples to then give away.

Then all worshipped Jesus
as enough loaves and fish
were given to everyone there.
But Jesus just watched them,
and smiled at the lad
who'd given his lunch-box
for Jesus to share.

2

Abba Father, let me be
Yours and Yours alone.
May my will for ever be
evermore Your own.
Never let my heart grow cold,
never let me go,
Abba Father, let me be
Yours and Yours alone.

3

Alleluia, alleluia,
give thanks to the risen Lord;
alleluia, alleluia,
give praise to His name.

Jesus is Lord of all the earth,
He is the King of creation.
Alleluia, alleluia . . .

Spread the good news through all the earth,
Jesus has died and has risen.
Alleluia, alleluia . . .

3 We have been crucified with Christ;
now we shall live for ever.
Alleluia, alleluia . . .

4 God has proclaimed the just reward,
life for all men, alleluia.
Alleluia, alleluia . . .

5 Come let us praise the living God,
joyfully sing to our Saviour:
Alleluia, alleluia . . .

4

1 **All people that on earth do dwell,**
sing to the Lord with cheerful voice:
serve Him with joy, His praises tell,
come now before Him and rejoice!
Know that the Lord is God indeed,
He formed us all without our aid;
we are the flock He loves to feed,
the sheep who by His hand are made.

2 O enter then His gates with praise,
and in His courts His love proclaim;
give thanks and bless Him all your days:
let every tongue confess His name.
The Lord our mighty God is good,
His mercy is for ever sure;
His truth at all times firmly stood,
and shall from age to age endure.

3 All people that on earth do dwell
sing to the Lord with cheerful voice:
serve Him with joy, His praises tell,
come now before Him and rejoice!
Praise God the Father, God the Son,
and God the Spirit evermore;
all praise to God, the Three-in-One,
let heaven rejoice and earth adore!

5

1 **All over the world the Spirit is moving,**
all over the world
as the prophet said it would be;
all over the world there's a mighty revelation
of the glory of the Lord,
as the waters cover the sea.

2 All over His Church God's Spirit is moving,
all over His Church
as the prophet said it would be;
all over His Church
there's a mighty revelation
of the glory of the Lord,
as the waters cover the sea.

3 Right here in this place the Spirit is moving,
right here in this place
as the prophet said it would be;
right here in this place
there's a mighty revelation
of the glory of the Lord,
as the waters cover the sea.

6 Cecil Frances Alexander (1818–95)

All things bright and beautiful,
all creatures great and small,
all things wise and wonderful,
the Lord God made them all.

1 Each little flower that opens,
each little bird that sings,
He made their glowing colours,
He made their tiny wings.
All things bright . . .

2 The purple-headed mountain,
the river running by,
the sunset, and the morning
that brightens up the sky;
All things bright . . .

3 The cold wind in the winter,
the pleasant summer sun,
the ripe fruits in the garden,
He made them every one.
All things bright . . .

4 He gave us eyes to see them,
and lips that we might tell
how great is God almighty,
who has made all things well.
All things bright . . .

7 © 1986 Greg Leavers

All around me, Lord, I see Your goodness,
all creation sings Your praises,
all the world cries, 'God is love!'

8 John Newton (1725–1807)

1 **Amazing grace – how sweet the sound –**
that saved a wretch like me!
I once was lost, but now am found,
was blind, but now I see.

2 'Twas grace that taught my heart to fear,
and grace my fears relieved;
how precious did that grace appear
the hour I first believed.

3 Through many dangers, toils and snares,
I have already come;
'tis grace has brought me safe thus far,
and grace will lead me home.

4 When we've been there ten thousand years
bright shining as the sun,
we've no less days to sing God's praise
than when we've first begun.

9 William Chatterton Dix (1837–98)
altered © 1986 Horrobin / Leavers

1 **As with gladness men of old**
did the guiding star behold;
as with joy they hailed its light,
leading onward, beaming bright,
so, most gracious God, may we
led by You for ever be.

2 As with joyful steps they sped,
Saviour, to Your lowly bed,
there to bend the knee before
You whom heaven and earth adore,
so may we with one accord,
seek forgiveness from our Lord.

3 As they offered gifts most rare,
gold and frankincense and myrrh,
so may we, cleansed from our sin,
lives of service now begin,
and in love our treasures bring,
Christ, to You our heavenly King.

4 Holy Jesus, every day
keep us in the narrow way;
and when earthly things are past,
bring our ransomed souls at last
where they need no star to guide,
where no clouds Your glory hide.

In the heavenly country bright
need they no created light;
You its light, its joy, its crown,
You its sun which goes not down.
There for ever may we sing
hallelujahs to our King.

James Montgomery (1771–1854)
© in this version Jubilate Hymns

Angels from the realms of glory,
wing your flight through all the earth;
heralds of creation's story
now proclaim Messiah's birth!
Come and worship
Christ, the new-born King;
come and worship,
worship Christ the new-born King.

Shepherds in the fields abiding,
watching by your flocks at night,
God with man is now residing:
see, there shines the infant light!
Come and worship . . .

Wise men, leave your contemplations!
brighter visions shine afar;
seek in Him the hope of nations,
you have seen His rising star:
Come and worship . . .

Though an infant now we view Him,
He will share His Father's throne,
gather all the nations to Him;
every knee shall then bow down:
Come and worship . . .

Anon
Copyright control

Ask! Ask! Ask! and it shall be given you;
Seek! Seek! Seek! and you shall find;
Knock! Knock! Knock!
    it shall be opened unto you,
your heavenly Father is so kind.
He knows what is best for His children
in body, soul and mind;
So ask! Ask! Ask! Knock! Knock! Knock!
Seek and you shall find.

12 verses 1 and 2: Anon
verse 3: J T McFarland (c1906)

1 **Away in a manger, no crib for a bed,**
the little Lord Jesus
    laid down His sweet head;
the stars in the bright sky
    looked down where He lay;
the little Lord Jesus asleep in the hay.

2 The cattle are lowing, the baby awakes,
but little Lord Jesus, no crying He makes:
I love You, Lord Jesus!
    look down from the sky
and stay by my side until morning is nigh.

3 Be near me, Lord Jesus; I ask You to stay
close by me for ever and love me, I pray;
bless all the dear children
    in Your tender care,
and fit us for heaven to live with You there.

13 Caroline Maria Noel (1817–77)
altered © 1986 Horrobin / Leavers

1 **At the name of Jesus**
every knee shall bow,
every tongue confess Him
King of glory now.
'Tis the Father's pleasure
we should call Him Lord,
who from the beginning
was the mighty Word.

2 Humbled for a season,
to receive a name
from the lips of sinners
unto whom He came,
faithfully He lived here
spotless to the last,
raised was He victorious,
when from death He passed.

3 Lifted high, triumphant,
far above the world,
into heaven's glory,
our ascended Lord;
to the throne of Godhead,
at the Father's side,
there He reigns resplendent
who for man had died.

4 In your hearts enthrone Him;
there let Him subdue
all that is not holy,
all that is not true;
crown Him as your captain
in temptation's hour,
let His will enfold you
in its light and power.

5 Brothers, this Lord Jesus
shall return again,
with His Father's glory,
with His angel-train;
for all wreaths of empire
meet upon His brow,
and our hearts confess Him
King of glory now.

14 Morris Chapman
© 1983 Word Music Inc / Word Music (UK) /
CopyCare Ltd

Be bold, be strong,
for the Lord your God is with you;
be bold, be strong,
for the Lord your God is with you!
I am not afraid, (No! No! No!)
I am not dismayed, (Not me!)
for I'm walking in faith and victory:
come on and walk in faith and victory,
for the Lord your God is with you.

15 Patricia van Tine
© 1978 Maranatha! Music / CopyCare Ltd

**Behold, what manner of love
the Father has given unto us,**
Behold, what manner of love
the Father has given unto us,
that we should be called the sons of God,
that we should be called the sons of God.

16 Graham Kendrick
© 1986 Kingsway's Thankyou Music

1 **Big man standing by the blue waterside,**
mending nets by the blue sea.
Along came Jesus, He said,
'Simon Peter, won't you leave your nets
and come, follow me.'

*You don't need anything,
I've got everything,
but, Peter, it's going to be a hard way.
You don't have to worry now,
come on and hurry now,
I'll walk beside you every day.*

2 Life wasn't easy for the big fisherman,
but still he followed till his dying day.
Along came Jesus, He said,
'Simon Peter, there's a place in heaven
where you can stay.'
You don't need anything . . .

17 Bob Gillman
© 1977 Kingsway's Thankyou Music

Bind us together, Lord,
*bind us together
with cords that cannot be broken;
bind us together, Lord,
bind us together,
O bind us together with love.*

1 There is only one God,
there is only one King,
there is only one body –
that is why we sing:
Bind us together . . .

2 Made for the glory of God,
purchased by His precious Son.
Born with the right to be clean,
for Jesus the victory has won.
Bind us together . . .

3 You are the family of God,
You are the promise divine,
You are God's chosen desire,
You are the glorious new wine.
Bind us together . . .

18 © 1986 Peter Horrobin

1 **Barabbas was a bad man,**
condemned to die was he,
he'd done so many awful things,
was bad as bad could be.

2 But Jesus was a good man,
God's only Son was He.
He did so many lovely things –
the blind He made to see.

But Jesus some folk hated,
they called, 'Put Him away!'
when Pilate made them choose the one
to free, that fatal day.

So Jesus, though a good man,
was killed on Calvary,
but three days on, He rose again
to live eternally.

9 From Psalm 103
Copyright control

Bless the Lord, O my soul,
bless the Lord, O my soul,
and all that is within me
bless His holy name.
Bless the Lord, O my soul,
bless the Lord, O my soul,
and all that is within me
bless His holy name.

King of kings (for ever and ever),
Lord of lords (for ever and ever),
King of kings (for ever and ever),
King of kings and Lord of lords!

Bless the Lord, O my soul . . .

0 Frances van Alstyne (1820–1915)
(Fanny J Crosby)

Blessèd assurance, Jesus is mine:
O what a foretaste of glory divine!
Heir of salvation, purchase of God;
born of His Spirit, washed in His blood.
  This is my story, this is my song,
  praising my Saviour all the day long;
  this is my story, this is my song,
  praising my Saviour all the day long.

Perfect submission, perfect delight,
visions of rapture burst on my sight;
angels descending, bring from above
echoes of mercy, whispers of love.
  This is my story . . .

Perfect submission, all is at rest,
I in my Saviour am happy and blest;
watching and waiting, looking above,
filled with His goodness, lost in His love.
  This is my story . . .

21 © 1981 Roger Jones /
National Christian Education Council

1 **Brothers and sisters**
in Jesus our Lord,
brothers and sisters,
believing His word!
Now we're united,
made one in His love,
we're brothers and sisters
in Jesus our Lord!

2 Jesus has saved us,
from sin set us free.
Always His people
together we'll be!
This is the story
we're telling the world,
we're brothers and sisters
in Jesus our Lord!

3 Jesus has told us
to be of good cheer,
for He is with us,
His Spirit is here!
He gives us power
His message to share.
We're brothers and sisters
in Jesus our Lord!

22 Anon
Copyright control

1 **Be still and know that I am God.**
Be still and know that I am God.
Be still and know that I am God.

2 I am the Lord that healeth thee.
I am the Lord that healeth thee.
I am the Lord that healeth thee.

3 In Thee, O Lord, I put my trust.
In Thee, O Lord, I put my trust.
In Thee, O Lord, I put my trust.

23 E H Swinstead (d1976)
Copyright control

By blue Galilee Jesus walked of old,
by blue Galilee wondrous things He told.
Saviour, still my teacher be,
showing wondrous things to me
as of old by Galilee, blue Galilee.

24 John Henley (1800–42)
altered © 1986 Horrobin / Leavers

1 **Children of Jerusalem**
sang the praise of Jesus' name;
children, too, of modern days,
join to sing the Saviour's praise:
Hark, hark, hark!
while children's voices sing,
hark, hark, hark!
while children's voices sing
loud hosannas, loud hosannas,
loud hosannas to our King.

2 We are taught to love the Lord,
we are taught to read His word,
we are taught the way to heaven;
praise for all to God be given:
Hark, hark, hark . . .

3 Parents, teachers, old and young,
all unite to swell the song;
higher let God's praises rise,
as hosannas fill the skies:
Hark, hark, hark . . .

25 © Michael Saward / Jubilate Hymns

1 **Christ triumphant, ever reigning,**
Saviour, Master, King,
Lord of heaven, our lives sustaining,
hear us as we sing:
Yours the glory and the crown,
the high renown, the eternal name.

2 Word incarnate, truth revealing,
Son of Man on earth!
power and majesty concealing
by your humble birth:
Yours the glory . . .

3 Suffering servant, scorned, ill-treated,
victim crucified!
death is through the cross defeated,
sinners justified:
Yours the glory . . .

4 Priestly King, enthroned for ever
high in heaven above!
sin and death and hell shall never
stifle hymns of love:
Yours the glory . . .

5 So, our hearts and voices raising
through the ages long,
ceaselessly upon You gazing,
this shall be our song:
Yours the glory . . .

26 Jimmy Owens
©1972 Bud John Songs / Alliance Media Ltd / CopyCare

Clap your hands, all you people,
shout unto God with a voice of triumph,
clap your hands, all you people,
shout unto God with a voice of praise!
Hosanna, hosanna,
shout unto God with a voice of triumph,
praise Him, praise Him,
shout unto God with a voice of praise!

27 R Hudson Pope (1879–1967)
© Scripture Gift Mission

Cleanse me from my sin, Lord,
put Your power within, Lord,
take me as I am, Lord,
and make me all Your own.
Keep me day by day, Lord,
in Your perfect way, Lord,
make my heart Your palace,
and Your royal throne.

28 Sue McClellan, John Paculabo, Keith Ryecroft
© 1974 Kingsway's Thankyou Music

1 **Colours of day dawn into the mind,**
the sun has come up, the night is behind.
Go down in the city, into the street,
and let's give the message
to the people we meet.
So light up the fire and let the flame burn,
open the door, let Jesus return.
Take seeds of His Spirit, let the fruit grow,
tell the people of Jesus, let His love show.

2 Go through the park, on into the town;
the sun still shines on, it never goes down.
The Light of the world is risen again,
the people of darkness
are needing our friend.
So light up the fire . . .

Open your eyes, look into the sky,
the darkness has come, the sun came to die,
the evening draws on, the sun disappears,
but Jesus is living, His Spirit is near.
So light up the fire . . .

29
Robert Walmsley (1831–1905)
altered © 1986 Horrobin / Leavers

Come, let us sing of a wonderful love,
faithful and true;
out of the heart of the Father above,
streaming to me and to you:
wonderful love
dwells in the heart of the Father above.

Jesus, the Saviour, this gospel to tell,
joyfully came;
came with the helpless
      and hopeless to dwell,
sharing their sorrow and shame;
seeking the lost,
saving, redeeming at measureless cost.

Jesus is seeking all lost people yet;
why can't they see?
Turning to Him, He forgives and forgets,
longing to set their hearts free.
Wonderful love
dwells in the heart of the Father above.

Come fill my heart with Your wonderful love,
come and abide,
lifting my life till it rises above
envy and falsehood and pride;
seeking to live
life that is humble,
      with strength that You give.

0
Anon
Copyright control

Come, listen to my tale
of Jonah and the whale,
way down in the middle of the ocean.
Well, how did he get there?
Whatever did he wear?
Way down in the middle of the ocean.
A-preaching he should be
at Nineveh, you see –
to disobey's a very foolish notion.
But God forgave his sin,
salvation entered in,
way down in the middle of the
way down in the middle of the
way down in the middle of the ocean.

31
Graham Kendrick
© 1986 Kingsway's Thankyou Music

Come on, let's get up and go,
let everyone know.
We've got a reason to shout and to sing
'cause Jesus loves us
and that's a wonderful thing.

Go! go! go! go! get up and go,
don't be sleepy or slow!
You, you, you, you know what to do,
give your life to Him.

Come on, let's get up and go . . .

32
Henry Alford (1810–71)
© in this version Jubilate Hymns

1 **Come, you thankful people, come,**
   raise the song of harvest home!
   Fruit and crops are gathered in
   safe before the storms begin:
   God our maker will provide
   for our needs to be supplied;
   come, with all His people, come,
   raise the song of harvest home!

2 All the world is God's own field,
   harvests for His praise to yield;
   wheat and weeds together sown
   here for joy or sorrow grown:
   first the blade and then the ear,
   then the full corn shall appear –
   Lord of harvest, grant that we
   wholesome grain and pure may be.

3 For the Lord our God shall come
   and shall bring His harvest home;
   He Himself on that great day,
   worthless things shall take away,
   give His angels charge at last
   in the fire the weeds to cast,
   but the fruitful ears to store
   in His care for evermore.

4 Even so, Lord, quickly come –
   bring Your final harvest home!
   Gather all Your people in
   free from sorrow, free from sin,
   there together purified,
   ever thankful at Your side –
   come, with all Your angels, come,
   bring that glorious harvest home!

33

'Come to Jesus, He's amazing!'
people cried out when they saw
people walking who were crippled,
blind eyes seeing, healed once more.

34

Come and praise the Lord our King,
hallelujah,
come and praise the Lord our King,
hallelujah.

1 Christ was born in Bethlehem, hallelujah,
Son of God and Son of Man, hallelujah.
Come and praise . . .

2 From Him love and wisdom came, hallelujah,
all His life was free from blame, hallelujah.
Come and praise . . .

3 Jesus died at Calvary, hallelujah,
rose again triumphantly, hallelujah.
Come and praise . . .

4 He will cleanse us from our sin, hallelujah,
if we live by faith in Him, hallelujah.
Come and praise . . .

5 He will be with us today, hallelujah,
and for ever with us stay, hallelujah.
Come and praise . . .

6 We will live with Him one day, hallelujah,
and for ever with Him stay, hallelujah.
Come and praise . . .

35

Deep and wide, deep and wide,
there's a fountain flowing deep and wide;
deep and wide, deep and wide,
there's a fountain flowing deep and wide.

36

Daniel was a man of prayer,
daily he prayed three times.
Till one day they had him cast
into a den of lions.
In the den, in the den,
fear could not alarm him.
God just shut the lions' mouths
so they could not harm him.

37

1 **Dear Lord and Father of mankind,**
forgive our foolish ways;
re-clothe us in our rightful mind;
in purer lives Your service find,
in deeper reverence, praise.

2 In simple trust like theirs who heard,
beside the Syrian sea,
the gracious calling of the Lord,
let us, like them, obey His word:
'Rise up and follow Me!'

3 O Sabbath rest by Galilee!
O calm of hills above,
where Jesus shared on bended knee
the silence of eternity,
interpreted by love!

4 With that deep hush subduing all
our words and works that drown
the tender whisper of Your call,
as noiseless let Your blessing fall,
as fell Your manna down.

5 Drop Your still dews of quietness,
till all our strivings cease;
take from our souls the strain and stress,
and let our ordered lives confess
the beauty of Your peace.

6 Breathe through the heats of our desire
Your coolness and Your balm;
let sense be dumb, let flesh retire;
speak through the earthquake,
    wind, and fire,
O still small voice of calm!

38

1 **Ding dong! Merrily on high**
in heaven the bells are ringing.
Ding dong! Verily the sky
is riven with angels singing:

Gloria, hosanna in excelsis;
gloria, hosanna in excelsis!

2 E'en so, here below, below,
let steeple bells be swungen,
and i-o, i-o, i-o,
by priest and people sungen!
Gloria . . .

3 Pray you, dutifully prime
your matin chime, ye ringers;
may you beautifully rime
your eve-time song, ye singers:
Gloria . . .

2 Not for ever in green pastures
do we ask our way to be;
but the steep and rugged pathway
may we tread rejoicingly.

3 Not for ever by still waters
would we idly rest and stay;
but would smite the living fountains
from the rocks along our way.

4 Be our strength in hours of weakness,
in our wanderings be our guide;
through endeavour, failure, danger,
Father, always at our side.

42
Jenny Hewer
© 1975 Kingsway's Thankyou Music

1 **Father, I place into Your hands**
the things that I can't do.
Father, I place into Your hands
the times that I've been through.
Father, I place into Your hands
the way that I should go,
for I know I always can trust You.

2 Father, I place into Your hands
my friends and family.
Father, I place into Your hands
the things that trouble me.
Father, I place into Your hands
the person I would be,
for I know I always can trust You.

3 Father, we love to seek Your face,
we love to hear Your voice.
Father, we love to sing Your praise,
and in Your name rejoice.
Father, we love to walk with You
and in Your presence rest,
for we know we always can trust You.

4 Father, I want to be with You
and do the things You do.
Father, I want to speak the words
that You are speaking too.
Father, I want to love the ones
that You will draw to You,
for I know that I am one with You.

39
Karen Lafferty
© 1981 Maranatha! Music / CopyCare Ltd

Don't build your house on the sandy land,
don't build it too near the shore.
Well, it might look kind of nice,
but you'll have to build it twice,
oh, you'll have to build your house
once more.
You'd better build your house upon a rock,
make a good foundation on a solid spot.
Oh, the storms may come and go,
but the peace of God you will know.

Rock of ages, cleft for me,
let me hide myself in Thee.

0
E H Swinstead (d1976)
Copyright control

Do you want a pilot?
Signal then to Jesus;
do you want a pilot?
Bid Him come on board.
For He will safely guide
across the ocean wide,
until you reach at last
the heavenly harbour.

1
Love Maria Willis (1824–1908)

Father, hear the prayer we offer:
not for ease that prayer shall be,
but for strength, that we may ever
live our lives courageously.

43
J P Hopps (1834–1912)
altered © 1986 Horrobin / Leavers

1 **Father, lead me day by day**
ever in your own good way;
teach me to be pure and true –
show me what I ought to do.

2 When in danger, make me brave;
   make me know that You can save.
   Keep me safe by Your dear side;
   let me in Your love abide.

3 When I'm tempted to do wrong,
   make me steadfast, wise and strong;
   and when all alone I stand,
   shield me with Your mighty hand.

4 When my work seems hard and dry,
   may I never cease to try;
   help me patiently to bear
   pain and hardship, toil and care.

5 May I do the good I know,
   be Your loving child below,
   then at last in heaven share
   life with You that's free from care.

44 Terrye Coelho
© 1972 Maranatha! Music / CopyCare Ltd

1 **Father, we adore You,**
   lay our lives before You:
   how we love You!

2 Jesus, we adore You,
   lay our lives before You:
   how we love You!

3 Spirit, we adore You,
   lay our lives before You:
   how we love You!

45 Donna Adkins
© 1976, 1981 Maranatha! Music / CopyCare Ltd

1 **Father, we love You,**
   we worship and adore You:
   glorify Your name
   in all the earth.
   Glorify Your name,
   glorify Your name,
   glorify Your name
   in all the earth.

2 Jesus, we love You,
   we worship and adore You:
   glorify Your name
   in all the earth.
   Glorify Your name,
   glorify Your name,
   glorify Your name
   in all the earth.

3 Spirit, we love You,
   we worship and adore You:
   glorify Your name
   in all the earth.
   Glorify Your name,
   glorify Your name,
   glorify Your name
   in all the earth.

46 © 1986 Greg Leavers

'Follow Me,' says Jesus,
'I can keep you safe.
I am the good shepherd,
so why not be My sheep?
If you're lost and lonely
I can keep you safe.
I gave My life to save you,
so come, just follow Me.'

47 Dave Richards
© 1977 Kingsway's Thankyou Music

For I'm building a people of power
and I'm making a people of praise,
that will move through this land
        by My Spirit,
and will glorify My precious name.
Build Your Church, Lord,
make us strong, Lord,
join our hearts, Lord, through Your Son;
make us one, Lord, in Your body,
in the kingdom of Your Son.

48 Folliott Pierpoint (1835–1917)
altered © 1986 Horrobin / Leavers

1 **For the beauty of the earth,**
   for the beauty of the skies,
   for the love which from our birth
   over and around us lies;
   Father, unto You we raise
   this our sacrifice of praise.

2 For the beauty of each hour
   of the day and of the night,
   hill and vale, and tree and flower,
   sun and moon, and stars of light;
   Father, unto You we raise
   this our sacrifice of praise.

3 For the joy of love from God,
that we share on earth below;
for our friends and family,
and the love that they can show;
Father, unto You we raise
this our sacrifice of praise.

4 For each perfect gift divine
to our race so freely given,
thank You, Lord, that they are mine,
here on earth as gifts from heaven;
Father, unto You we raise
this our sacrifice of praise.

49
From Psalm 113
© Paul S Deeming / Integrity's Hosanna! Music /
Kingsway's Thankyou Music

From the rising of the sun
to the going down of the same,
the Lord's name is to be praised.
From the rising of the sun
to the going down of the same,
the Lord's name is to be praised.
Praise ye the Lord,
praise Him, O ye servants of the Lord,
praise the name of the Lord;
blessèd be the name of the Lord
from this time forth,
and for evermore.

50
A Sevison
Copyright control

Give me oil in my lamp, keep me burning,
give me oil in my lamp, I pray;
give me oil in my lamp, keep me burning,
keep me burning till the break of day.
Sing hosanna, sing hosanna,
sing hosanna to the King of kings!
Sing hosanna, sing hosanna,
sing hosanna to the King!

Give me joy in my heart, keep me singing,
give me joy in my heart, I pray;
give me joy in my heart, keep me singing,
keep me singing till the break of day.
Sing hosanna . . .

Give me love in my heart, keep me serving,
give me love in my heart, I pray;
give me love in my heart, keep me serving,
keep me serving till the break of day.
Sing hosanna . . .

4 Give me peace in my heart, keep me resting,
give me peace in my heart, I pray;
give me peace in my heart, keep me resting,
keep me resting till the break of day.
Sing hosanna . . .

51
© 1986 Greg Leavers

Glory to God in the highest,
peace upon earth,
Jesus Christ has come to earth;
that's why we sing,
'Jesus the King,
Jesus has come for you.'

1 The shepherds who were sitting there
were suddenly filled with fear;
the dark night was filled with light,
angels singing everywhere.
Glory to God . . .

2 The next time we hear a song
of worship from a heavenly throng,
will be when Jesus comes again,
then with triumph we'll all sing:
Glory to God . . .

52
Thomas Ken (1637–1711)
© in this version Jubilate Hymns

1 **Glory to You, my God, this night**
for all the blessings of the light;
keep me, O keep me, King of kings,
beneath Your own almighty wings.

2 Forgive me, Lord, through Your dear Son,
the wrong that I this day have done,
that peace with God and man may be,
before I sleep, restored to me.

3 Teach me to live, that I may dread
the grave as little as my bed;
teach me to die, that so I may
rise glorious at the awesome day.

4 O may my soul on you repose
and restful sleep my eyelids close;
sleep that shall me more vigorous make
to serve my God when I awake.

5 If in the night I sleepless lie,
my mind with peaceful thoughts supply;
let no dark dreams disturb my rest,
no powers of evil me molest.

6 Praise God from whom all blessings flow
in heaven above and earth below;
one God, three persons, we adore –
to Him be praise for evermore!

53 Anon
Copyright control

1 **God is so good,**
God is so good,
God is so good,
He's so good to me.

2 He took my sin,
He took my sin,
He took my sin,
He's so good to me.

3 Now I am free,
now I am free,
now I am free,
He's so good to me.

4 God is so good,
He took my sin,
now I am free,
He's so good to me.

54 Carol Owens
© 1972 Bud John Songs / Alliance Media Ltd /
CopyCare Ltd

1 **God forgave my sin in Jesus' name;**
I've been born again in Jesus' name,
and in Jesus' name I come to you
to share His love as He told me to.
He said:
'Freely, freely you have received,
freely, freely give;
go in My name and because you believe,
others will know that I live.'

2 All power is given in Jesus' name
in earth and heaven in Jesus' name;
and in Jesus' name I come to you
to share His power as He told me to.
He said . . .

55 Graham Kendrick
© 1985 Kingsway's Thankyou Music

God is good – we sing and shout it,
God is good – we celebrate;
God is good – no more we doubt it,
God is good – we know it's true!

And when I think of His love for me,
my heart fills with praise
and I feel like dancing;
for in His heart there is room for me,
and I run with arms opened wide.

God is good – we sing and shout it,
God is good – we celebrate;
God is good – no more we doubt it,
God is good – we know it's true! *Hey!*

56 © Christopher Porteous / Jubilate Hymns

1 **God is our guide, our light**
and our deliverer,
He holds our hand,
He walks beside the way.
Lord, may our feet tread
in the steps You taught us
to follow firmly as by faith each day,
Your word a light,
a lamp to lead our footsteps –
we love the hours when You beside us stay.

2 God is our peace,
our help and our protector,
we find His presence in the hour of need.
Lord, though the storms of life
may leave us trembling,
Your words of comfort bring us peace within
When we are weak
and fear to face the future
we find such comfort in Your loving arms.

3 God is our hope, our joy and our salvation,
His love alone transforms the sinful heart.
Lord, how we sought Your Spirit's
sweet renewing:
Your healing touch has filled our hearts
with praise.
We come and worship Jesus,
Lord and Saviour,
His love alone must fill our earthly days.

4 God is our strength,
our rock and our redeemer
in times of trouble and in times of joy.
Lord, may our lives be full
of sure thanksgiving,
our lips be full of symphonies of praise.
You gave us love, a risen, living Saviour,
we bring ourselves, a sacrifice of praise.

57 Arthur Campbell Ainger (1841–1919)
© in this version Jubilate Hymns

1 **God is working His purpose out,**
as year succeeds to year:
God is working His purpose out,
and the time is drawing near:
nearer and nearer draws the time,
the time that shall surely be,
when the earth shall be filled
with the glory of God,
as the waters cover the sea.

2 From utmost east to utmost west
wherever man has trod,
by the mouth of many messengers
rings out the voice of God:
listen to me, you continents,
you islands, look to me,
that the earth may be filled
with the glory of God,
as the waters cover the sea.

3 We shall march in the strength of God,
with the banner of Christ unfurled,
that the light of the glorious gospel of truth
may shine throughout the world;
we shall fight with sorrow and sin
to set their captives free,
that the earth may be filled
with the glory of God,
as the waters cover the sea.

All we can do is nothing worth
unless God blesses the deed;
vainly we hope for the harvest-tide
till God gives life to the seed:
nearer and nearer draws the time,
the time that shall surely be,
when the earth shall be filled
with the glory of God,
as the waters cover the sea.

8 Gloria and William J Gaither
© 1971 Coronation Music Publishing /
Kingsway's Thankyou Music

God sent His Son, they call Him Jesus;
He came to love, heal, and forgive;
He lived and died to buy my pardon,
an empty grave is there
   to prove my Saviour lives.

Because He lives I can face tomorrow;
because He lives all fear is gone;
because I know, I know
   He holds the future,
and life is worth the living
   just because He lives.

2 How sweet to hold a new-born baby,
and feel the pride and joy he gives;
but greater still the calm assurance,
this child can face uncertain days
   because He lives.
   Because He lives . . .

3 And then one day I'll cross the river;
I'll fight life's final war with pain;
and then as death gives way to victory,
I'll see the lights of glory
   and I'll know He lives.
   Because He lives . . .

59 © 1986 Peter Horrobin

1 **God so loved the world**
   He sent to us Jesus,
God so loved the world He sent His Son.
Alleluia, Jesus, Lord Jesus, Jesus,
alleluia, Jesus, God sent His Son.

2 Jesus showed the world the love
   of the Father,
Jesus showed the world how we must love.
Alleluia, Jesus, Lord Jesus, Jesus,
alleluia, Jesus, God sent His Son.

60 Anon
Altered © 1986 Horrobin / Leavers

God's not dead (no),
He is alive,
God's not dead (no),
He is alive,
God's not dead (no),
He is alive!
Serve Him with my hands,
follow with my feet,
love Him in my heart,
know Him in my life;
for He's alive in me.

61 John Arlott (1914–91)
© Mrs B M Arlott / W S V Kennard

1 **God, whose farm is all creation,**
take the gratitude we give;
take the finest of our harvest,
crops we grow that men may live.

2 Take our ploughing, seeding, reaping,
hopes and fears of sun and rain,
all our thinking, planning, waiting,
ripened in this fruit and grain.

3 All our labour, all our watching,
all our calendar of care,
in these crops of Your creation,
take, O God; they are our prayer.

62 © 1986 Peter Horrobin

1 **God whose Son was once a man on earth**
gave His life that men may live.
Risen, our ascended Lord
fulfilled His promised word.
  When the Spirit came,
    the Church was born,
  God's people shared
    in a bright new dawn.
  They healed the sick,
  they taught God's word,
  they sought the lost,
  they obeyed the Lord.
  And it's all because the Spirit came
  that the world will never be the same,
  because the Spirit came.

2 God whose power fell on the early church,
sent to earth from heaven above;
Spirit-led, by Him ordained,
they showed the world God's love.
  When the Spirit came . . .

3 Pour Your Spirit on the church today,
that Your life through me may flow;
Spirit-filled, I'll serve Your name
and live the truth I know.
  When the Spirit comes, new life is born,
  God's people share in a bright new dawn.
  We'll heal the sick,
  we'll teach God's word,
  we'll seek the lost,
  we'll obey the Lord.
  And it's all because the Spirit came
  that the world will never be the same,
  because the Spirit came.

63 Sarah Betts Rhodes (1829–1904)
altered © 1986 Horrobin / Leavers

1 **God, who made the earth,**
the air, the sky, the sea,
who gave the light its birth,
will care for me.

2 God, who made the grass,
the flower, the fruit, the tree,
the day and night to pass,
will care for me.

3 God, who made the sun,
the moon, the stars, is He
who, when life's clouds come on,
will care for me.

4 God, who sent His son
to die on Calvary,
He, if I lean on Him,
will care for me.

5 God, who gave me life
His servant here to be,
has promised in His word
to care for me.

64 Thomas O Chisholm (1866–1960)
© 1923, 1951 Hope Publishing / CopyCare Ltd
in this version Jubilate Hymns

1 **Great is Your faithfulness,**
  O God my Father,
You have fulfilled all Your promise to me;
You never fail and Your love is unchanging;
all You have been You for ever will be.
  Great is Your faithfulness,
  great is Your faithfulness;
  morning by morning
  new mercies I see;
  all I have needed
  Your hand has provided –
  great is Your faithfulness,
  Father, to me!

2 Summer and winter,
    and spring-time and harvest,
sun, moon and stars in their courses above
join with all nature in eloquent witness
to Your great faithfulness, mercy and love.
  Great is Your faithfulness . . .

3 Pardon for sin, and a peace everlasting,
Your living presence to cheer and to guide

strength for today
and bright hope for tomorrow,
these are the blessings
Your love will provide.
Great is Your faithfulness . . .

65

Go, tell it on the mountain,
over the hills and everywhere;
go, tell it on the mountain
that Jesus is His name.

1 He possessed no riches,
no home to lay His head;
He saw the needs of others
and cared for them instead.
Go, tell it on the mountain . . .

2 He reached out and touched them,
the blind, the deaf, the lame;
He spoke and listened gladly
to anyone who came.
Go, tell it on the mountain . . .

3 Some turned away in anger,
with hatred in the eye;
they tried Him and condemned Him,
then led Him out to die.
Go, tell it on the mountain . . .

4 'Father, now forgive them' –
those were the words He said;
in three more days He was alive
and risen from the dead.
Go, tell it on the mountain . . .

5 He still comes to people,
His life moves through the lands;
He uses us for speaking,
He touches with our hands.
Go, tell it on the mountain . . .

66

Hallelujah! for the Lord our God
the almighty reigns.
Hallelujah! for the Lord our God
the almighty reigns.
Let us rejoice and be glad and give
the glory unto Him.
Hallelujah! for the Lord our God
the almighty reigns.

67
6|98

Hallelu, hallelu, hallelu, hallelujah;
we'll praise the Lord;
hallelu, hallelu, hallelu, hallelujah;
we'll praise the Lord!
We'll praise the Lord, hallelujah,
we'll praise the Lord, hallelujah,
we'll praise the Lord, hallelujah,
we'll praise the Lord!

68

1 **Hark, the glad sound! the Saviour comes,**
the Saviour promised long;
let every heart prepare a throne,
and every voice a song.

2 He comes, the prisoners to release
in Satan's bondage held;
the chains of sin before Him break,
the iron fetters yield.

3 He comes the broken heart to bind,
the wounded soul to cure;
and with the treasures of His grace
to enrich the humble poor.

4 Our glad hosannas, Prince of peace,
Your welcome shall proclaim;
and heaven's eternal arches ring
with Your belovèd name.

69

1 **Hark! the herald-angels sing,**
'Glory to the new-born King!'
Peace on earth, and mercy mild,
God and sinners reconciled.'
Joyful, all you nations rise,
join the triumph of the skies;
with the angelic host proclaim,
'Christ is born in Bethlehem!'
Hark! the herald-angels sing,
'Glory to the new-born King!'

2 Christ by highest heaven adored,
Christ, the everlasting Lord,
late in time behold Him come,
offspring of a virgin's womb!
Veiled in flesh the Godhead see!
Hail, the incarnate Deity!
Pleased as man with man to dwell,
Jesus, our Immanuel.
Hark! the herald-angels sing,
'Glory to the new-born King!'

3 Hail, the heaven-born Prince of peace!
Hail, the Sun of righteousness!
Light and life to all He brings,
risen with healing in His wings.
Mild He lays His glory by,
born that man no more may die;
born to raise the sons of earth,
born to give them second birth.
Hark! the herald-angels sing,
'Glory to the new-born King!'

70 Ira F Stanphill
© 1968 Singspiration Music / Fine Balance Music /
CopyCare Ltd

1 **Happiness is to know the Saviour,**
living a life within His favour,
having a change in my behaviour,
happiness is the Lord.

2 Happiness is a new creation,
Jesus and me in close relation,
having a part in His salvation,
happiness is the Lord.
Real joy is mine,
no matter if teardrops start;
I've found the secret –
it's Jesus in my heart!

3 Happiness is to be forgiven,
living a life that's worth the living,
taking a trip that leads to heaven,
happiness is the Lord,
happiness is the Lord,
happiness is the Lord!

71 Christian Strover
© M C T Strover / Jubilate Hymns

1 **Have you heard the raindrops**
   drumming on the rooftops?
Have you heard the raindrops
   dripping on the ground?
Have you heard the raindrops
   splashing in the streams
and running to the rivers all around?

There's water, water of life,
Jesus gives us the water of life,
there's water, water of life,
Jesus gives us the water of life.

2 There's a busy workman
   digging in the desert,
digging with a spade that flashes in the sun;
soon there will be water
   rising in the wellshaft,
spilling from the bucket as it comes.
There's water . . .

3 Nobody can live who hasn't any water,
when the land is dry
   then nothing much grows;
Jesus gives us life if we drink the living water,
sing it so that everybody knows.
There's water . . .

72 © P A Taylor

1 **Have you seen the pussy cat**
   sitting on the wall?
Have you heard his beautiful purr? (*purr*)
Have you seen the lion
   stalking round his prey?
Have you heard his terrible roar? (*roar*)
One so big, one so small,
our heavenly Father cares for them all,
one so big, one so small,
our heavenly Father cares.

2 Have you seen the children
   coming home from school?
Have you heard them shout,
'Hurray!' (*Hurray!*)
Have you seen the grown-ups
   coming home from work,
saying, 'What a horrible day!'
(*What a horrible day!*)
Some so big, some so small,
our heavenly Father cares for them all,
some so big, some so small,
our heavenly Father cares.

73 Anon
Copyright control

1 **He brought me to His banqueting house**
and His banner over me is love,
He brought me to His banqueting house
and His banner over me is love,
He brought me to His banqueting house
and His banner over me is love,
His banner over me is love.

God loves you and I love you
and that's the way it should be.
God loves you and I love you
and that's the way it should be.

2   He feeds me at His banqueting table . . .
    God loves you . . .

3   He lifts me up to the heavenly places . . .
    God loves you . . .

4   There's one way to peace through the power
    of the cross . . .
    God loves you . . .

5   Jesus is the rock of my salvation . . .
    God loves you . . .

74   Alan Pinnock
         © 1970 High-Fye Music Ltd

1   **He gave me eyes so I could see**
    the wonders of the world.
    Without my eyes I could not see
    the other boys and girls.
    He gave me ears so I could hear
    the wind and rain and sea.
    I've got to tell it to the world,
    He made me!

2   He gave me lips so I could speak,
    and say what's in my mind.
    Without my lips I could not speak
    a single word or line.
    He made my mind so I could think
    and choose what I should be.
    I've got to tell it to the world,
    He made me!

3   He gave me hands so I could touch,
    and hold a thousand things.
    I need my hands to help me write,
    to help me fetch and bring.
    These feet He made so I could run,
    He meant me to be free.
    I've got to tell it to the world,
    He made me!

75   Marvin Frey
         Copyright control

1   **He is Lord, He is Lord,**
    He is risen from the dead
    and He is Lord!
    Every knee shall bow,
    every tongue confess
    that Jesus Christ is Lord.

2   He's my Lord, He's my Lord,
    He is risen from the dead
    and He's my Lord!
    And my knee shall bow
    and my tongue confess
    that Jesus is my Lord.

76   © Archie Hall

He made the stars to shine,
He made the rolling sea,
He made the mountains high,
and He made me.
But this is why I love Him –
for me He bled and died,
the Lord of all creation
became the crucified.

77   Anon
         Copyright control

He paid a debt He did not owe,
I owed a debt I could not pay.
I needed someone to wash my sins away,
and now I sing a brand new song,
'Amazing grace!' the whole day long,
for Jesus paid a debt that I could never pay.

78   Anon
         © HarperCollins*Religious* / CopyCare Ltd

1   **He's got the whole wide world**
    in His hands,
    He's got the whole wide world in His hands,
    He's got the whole wide world in His hands,
    He's got the whole world in His hands.

2   He's got everybody here in His hands . . .

3   He's got the tiny little baby in His hands . . .

4   He's got you and me, brother,
    in His hands . . .

79   © 1986 Peter Horrobin and Greg Leavers

1   **He's great! He's God!**
    Jesus Christ is Lord.
    He's great! He's God!
    Trust His word.

2 His word is truth,
   for He cannot lie.
   His word is truth,
   to live by.

3 His love is strong,
   and will never end.
   His love is strong,
   praise His name.

4 He lives evermore
   as the King of kings.
   He lives evermore!
   Worship Him.

80 Percy Dearmer (1867–1936)
after John Bunyan (1628–88)
by permission of Oxford University Press

1 **He who would valiant be**
   'gainst all disaster,
   let him in constancy
   follow the Master.
   There's no discouragement
   shall make him once relent
   his first avowed intent
   to be a pilgrim.

2 Who so beset him round
   with dismal stories,
   do but themselves confound –
   his strength the more is.
   No foes shall stay his might,
   though he with giants fight:
   he will make good his right
   to be a pilgrim.

3 Since, Lord, Thou dost defend
   us with Thy Spirit,
   we know we at the end
   shall life inherit.
   Then fancies flee away!
   I'll fear not what men say,
   I'll labour night and day
   to be a pilgrim.

81 Israeli traditional song

Hévénu shalom aléchem,
Hévénu shalom aléchem,
Hévénu shalom aléchem,
Hévénu shalom,
shalom, shalom aléchem.

82 Anon
Copyright control

How great is our God,
how great is His name,
how great is His love
forever the same.

He rolled back the waters
of the mighty Red Sea,
and He said, 'I'll never leave you,
put your trust in Me.'

83 Hugh Mitchell
© 1973 Zondervan Corporation / Fine Balance Music /
CopyCare Ltd

How did Moses cross the Red Sea?
How did Moses cross the Red Sea?
How did Moses cross the Red Sea?
How did he get across?
Did he swim? No! No!
Did he row? No! No!
Did he jump? No! No! No! No!
Did he drive? No! No!
Did he fly? No! No!
How did he get across?
God blew with His wind, puff, puff, puff, puff.
He blew just enough, 'nough, 'nough,
   'nough, 'nough,
and through the sea He made a path –
that's how he got across.

84 Leonard E Smith Jnr
© 1974, 1978 New Jerusalem Music /
Kingsway's Thankyou Music

1 **How lovely on the mountains**
      are the feet of him
   who brings good news, good news,
   proclaiming peace,
      announcing news of happiness:
   our God reigns, our God reigns!
      Our God reigns, our God reigns,
      our God reigns, our God reigns!

2 You watchmen,
      lift your voices joyfully as one,
   shout for your King, your King.
   See eye to eye the Lord restoring Zion:
   your God reigns, your God reigns!
      Your God reigns, your God reigns,
      your God reigns, your God reigns!

3 Waste places of Jerusalem
    break forth with joy,
  we are redeemed, redeemed.
  The Lord has saved
    and comforted His people:
  your God reigns, your God reigns!
    Your God reigns, your God reigns,
    your God reigns, your God reigns!

4 Ends of the earth,
    see the salvation of your God,
  Jesus is Lord, is Lord.
  Before the nations
    He has bared His holy arm:
  your God reigns, your God reigns!
    Your God reigns, your God reigns,
    your God reigns, your God reigns!

85 John Drummond Burns (1823–64)
altered © 1986 Horrobin / Leavers

Hushed was the evening hymn,
the temple courts were dark;
the lamp was burning dim
before the sacred ark,
when suddenly a voice divine
rang through the silence of the shrine.

The old man, meek and mild,
the priest of Israel, slept;
his watch the temple child,
the little Samuel, kept:
and what from Eli's sense was sealed
the Lord to Hannah's son revealed.

O give me Samuel's ear,
the open ear, O Lord,
alive and quick to hear
each whisper of Your word –
like him to answer at Your call,
and to obey You first of all.

O give me Samuel's heart,
a lowly heart, that waits
to serve and play the part
You show us at Your gates,
by day and night, a heart that still
moves at the breathing of Your will.

O give me Samuel's mind,
a sweet, unmurmuring faith,
obedient and resigned
to You in life and death,
that I may read with childlike eyes
truths that are hidden from the wise.

86 Frances Ridley Havergal (1836–79)

1 **I am trusting You, Lord Jesus,**
  You have died for me;
  trusting You for full salvation,
  great and free.

2 I am trusting You for pardon,
  at Your feet I bow;
  for Your grace and tender mercy,
  trusting now.

3 I am trusting You for cleansing,
  Jesus, Son of God;
  trusting You to make me holy
  by Your blood.

4 I am trusting You to guide me;
  You alone shall lead,
  every day and hour supplying
  all my need.

5 I am trusting You for power,
  Yours can never fail;
  words which You Yourself shall give me
  must prevail.

6 I am trusting You, Lord Jesus;
  never let me fall;
  I am trusting You for ever,
  and for all.

87 Graham Kendrick
© 1985 Kingsway's Thankyou Music

I am a lighthouse,
    a shining and bright house,
out in the waves of a stormy sea.
The oil of the Spirit keeps my lamp burning:
Jesus my Lord is the light in me.
And when people see
    the good things that I do,
they'll give praise to God
    who has sent us Jesus.
We'll send out a lifeboat
    of love and forgiveness
and give them a hand to get in.
I am a lighthouse . . .

While the storm is raging, whoosh, whoosh,
and the wind is blowing, oooh, oooh,
and the waves are crashing,
    crash! crash! crash! crash!

I am a lighthouse,
    a shining and bright house,
out in the waves of a stormy sea.
The oil of the Spirit keeps my lamp burning:
Jesus my Lord is the light in me.

88 Philipp Bliss (1838–76)

1 **I am so glad that our Father in heaven**
tells of His love in the book He has given:
wonderful things in the Bible I see;
this is the dearest, that Jesus loves me.
   I am so glad that Jesus loves me,
   Jesus loves me, Jesus loves me,
   I am so glad that Jesus loves me,
   Jesus loves even me.

2 Though I forget Him, and wander away,
He'll always love me wherever I stray;
back to His dear loving arms do I flee,
when I remember that Jesus loves me.
   I am so glad . . .

3 Oh, if there's only one song I can sing,
when in His beauty I see the great King,
this shall my song in eternity be:
'O what a wonder that Jesus loves me!'
   I am so glad . . .

4 If one should ask of me, 'How can I tell?'
Glory to Jesus, I know very well;
God's Holy Spirit with mine does agree,
constantly witnessing: Jesus loves me.
   I am so glad . . .

89 Anon
Copyright control

'I am the way, the truth and the life,'
that's what Jesus said.
'I am the way, the truth and the life,'
that's what Jesus said.
Without the way there is no going,
without the truth there is no knowing,
without the life there is no living.
'I am the way, the truth and the life,'
that's what Jesus said.

90 Anon
Copyright control

I can run through a troop
and leap over a wall.
Hallelujah (glory, glory), hallelujah.
He's my Prince of peace,
He gives power to all.
Hallelujah (glory, glory), hallelujah.
Now there is no condemnation,
Jesus is the rock of my salvation.
I can run through a troop
and leap over a wall.
Hallelujah (glory, glory), hallelujah.

91 Sydney Carter
© 1963 Stainer & Bell Ltd

1 **I danced in the morning**
when the world was begun
and I danced in the moon
and the stars and the sun,
and I came down from heaven
and I danced on the earth –
at Bethlehem I had my birth.
   Dance, then, wherever you may be,
   I am the Lord of the dance, said He,
   and I'll lead you all, wherever you may be,
   and I'll lead you all in the dance, said He.

2 I danced for the scribe and the pharisee,
but they would not dance
and they wouldn't follow me.
I danced for the fishermen,
for James and John –
they came with me and the dance went on.
   Dance, then . . .

92 Alfred B Smith and Eugene Clarke
© 1958 Singspiration Music /
Fine Balance Music / CopyCare Ltd

1 **I do not know what lies ahead,**
the way I cannot see;
yet one stands near to be my guide,
He'll show the way to me:
   I know who holds the future,
   and He'll guide me with His hand;
   with God things don't just happen,
   everything by Him is planned.
   So as I face tomorrow,
   with its problems large and small,
   I'll trust the God of miracles,
   give to Him my all.

2 I do not know how many days
of life are mine to spend;
but one who knows and cares for me
will keep me to the end:
I know who holds . . .

3 I do not know the course ahead,
what joys and griefs are there;
but one is near who fully knows,
I'll trust His loving care:
I know who holds . . .

93 Rick Founds and Todd Collins
© 1982 Maranatha! Music / CopyCare Ltd

I'll be still and know that You are God;
I'll be still and know You are the Lord;
I'll be still to worship and adore You,
blessèd One, Emmanuel, Jesus.

94 Brian Howard
© 1974 Mission Hills Music /
Kingsway's Thankyou Music

If I were a butterfly,
I'd thank You, Lord, for giving me wings.
And if I were a robin in a tree,
I'd thank You, Lord, that I could sing.
And if I were a fish in the sea,
I'd wiggle my tail and I'd giggle with glee,
but I just thank you, Father,
for making me 'me'.
For You gave me a heart
and You gave me a smile,
You gave me Jesus
and You made me Your child,
and I just thank you, Father,
for making me 'me'.

If I were an elephant,
I'd thank You, Lord, by raising my trunk.
And if I were a kangaroo
You know I'd hop right up to You.
And if I were an octopus,
I'd thank You, Lord, for my fine looks,
but I just thank You, Father,
for making me 'me'.
For You gave me a heart . . .

3 If I were a wiggly worm,
I'd thank You, Lord, that I could squirm,
and if I were a billy goat,
I'd thank You, Lord, for my strong throat,
and if I were a fuzzy wuzzy bear,
I'd thank You, Lord, for my fuzzy wuzzy hair,
but I just thank You, Father,
for making me 'me'.
For You gave me a heart . . .

95 © 1981 Annie and Neil Simpson

1 **If you see someone lying in the road,**
don't leave him there, give him a hand.
If you see someone crying in the road,
don't leave him there, give him a hand.
Doesn't matter who you are;
you might be a tramp or a movie star.
Just remember, whoever you are,
that it's Jesus lying there,
that it's Jesus crying there.

2 If Jesus sees you lying in the road,
He won't leave you there,
he'll give you a hand.
If Jesus sees you crying in the road,
He won't leave you there,
he'll give you a hand.
Doesn't matter who you are;
you might be a tramp or a movie star.
Just remember, whoever you are,
that He sees you lying there,
and He sees you crying there.

96 © 1939 Joseph Carlson
Copyright control

If you want joy, real joy, wonderful joy,
let Jesus come into your heart.
If you want joy, real joy, wonderful joy,
let Jesus come into your heart.
Your sins He'll take away,
your night He'll turn to day,
your heart He'll make over anew,
and then come in to stay.
If you want joy, real joy, wonderful joy,
let Jesus come into your heart.

97 Anon
Copyright control

1 **I gotta home in gloryland**
    that outshines the sun,
  I gotta home in gloryland
      that outshines the sun,
  I gotta home in gloryland
      that outshines the sun,
  way beyond the blue.
    Do, Lord, O do, Lord, O do remember me;
    do, Lord, O do, Lord, O do remember me;
    do, Lord, O do, Lord, O do remember me,
    way beyond the blue.

2 I took Jesus as my Saviour,
      you take Him too . . .
    Do, Lord, O do, Lord . . .

3 If you will not bear a cross,
      you can't wear a crown . . .
    Do, Lord, O do, Lord . . .

98 An Indian prince
Copyright control

1 **I have decided to follow Jesus,** (*3 times*)
  no turning back, no turning back.

2 The world behind me, the cross before me,
    (*3 times*)
  no turning back, no turning back.

3 Though none go with me, I still will follow,
    (*3 times*)
  no turning back, no turning back.

4 Will you decide now to follow Jesus?
    (*3 times*)
  no turning back, no turning back.

99 Charlie Chester and Benny Litchfield
© 1970 High-Fye Music

1 **I have seen the golden sunshine,**
  I have watched the flowers grow,
  I have listened to the song birds
  and there's one thing now I know:
  they were all put there for us to share
  by someone so divine,
  and if you're a friend of Jesus
  (*clap, clap, clap, clap*)
  you're a friend of mine.
    I've seen the light, I've seen the light,
    and that's why my heart sings.
    I've known the joy, I've known the joy
    that loving Jesus brings.

2 I have seen the morning sunshine,
  I have heard the oceans roar,
  I have seen the flowers of springtime
  and there's one thing I am sure:
  they were all put there for us to share
  by someone so divine,
  and if you're a friend of Jesus
  (*clap, clap, clap, clap*)
  you're a friend of mine.
    I've seen the light . . .

100 Dave Moody
© 1984 C A Music / Music Services /
CopyCare Ltd

I hear the sound of the army of the Lord;
I hear the sound of the army of the Lord;
it's the sound of praise,
it's the sound of war;
the army of the Lord,
the army of the Lord,
the army of the Lord is marching on.

101 Anon
Copyright control

I may never march in the infantry,
ride with the cavalry, shoot with the artillery,
I may never zoom o'er the enemy,
for I'm in the Lord's army.
I'm in the Lord's army (Yes, sir!),
I'm in the Lord's army (Yes, sir!).
I may never march in the infantry,
ride with the cavalry, shoot with the artillery,
I may never zoom o'er the enemy,
for I'm in the Lord's army.

102 Anon
Copyright control

I met Jesus at the crossroads,
where the two ways meet.
Satan too was standing there,
and he said, 'Come this way!
Lots and lots of pleasures
I can give to you today.'
But I said, 'No, there's Jesus here,
just see what He offers me.
Down here, my sins forgiven,
up there, a home in heaven.
Praise God! That's the way for me.'

103

Eric A Thorn
© Christian Music Ministries

1 **I met You at the cross,**
Jesus, my Lord;
I heard You from that cross:
my name You called –
asked me to follow You all of my days,
asked me for evermore Your name to praise.

2 I saw You on the cross
dying for me;
I put You on that cross:
but Your one plea –
would I now follow You all of my days,
and would I evermore
    Your great name praise?

3 Jesus, my Lord and King,
Saviour of all,
Jesus the King of kings,
You heard my call –
that I would follow You all of my days,
and that for evermore Your name I'd praise.

104 Anon
altered © 1986 Horrobin / Leavers

I'm feeding on the living bread,
I'm drinking at the fountain head;
for all who drink, so Jesus said,
will never, never thirst again.
What, never thirst again?
No! never thirst again.
What, never thirst again?
No! never thirst again.
For all who drink, so Jesus said,
will never, never thirst again.

105 Oswald J Smith
© 1952 Zondervan Corporation /
Fine Balance Music / CopyCare Ltd

1 **I'm singing for my Lord everywhere I go,**
singing of His wondrous love,
    that the world may know
how He saved a wretch like me
    by His death on Calvary:
I'm singing for my Lord everywhere I go.

2 I'm singing, but sometimes heavy is the rod,
for this world is not a friend
    to the grace of God.
Yet I sing the whole day long,
    for He fills my heart with song,
I'm singing for my Lord everywhere I go.

3 I'm singing for the lost just because I know
Jesus Christ, whose precious blood
    washes white as snow.
If my songs to Him can bring
    some lost soul I'll gladly sing:
I'm singing for my Lord everywhere I go.

4 I'm singing for the saints
    as they journey home;
soon they'll reach that happy land
    where they'll never roam.
And with me they'll join and sing
    praises to our Lord and King:
I'm singing for my Lord everywhere I go.

106 Graham Kendrick
© 1986 Kingsway's Thankyou Music

I'm special because God has loved me,
for He gave the best thing that He had
    to save me:
His own Son Jesus,
    crucified to take the blame,
for all the bad things I have done.

Thank You, Jesus, thank You, Lord,
for loving me so much;
I know I don't deserve anything,
help me feel Your love right now,
to know deep in my heart
    that I'm Your special friend.

107 Alice M Pullen
© D M Gill

1 **I'm very glad of God:**
His love takes care of me.
In every lovely thing I see
God smiles at me.

2 I'm very glad of God:
His love takes care of me.
In every lovely sound I hear
God speaks to me.

108 W G Wills (1841–91)
altered © 1986 Horrobin / Leavers

1 **In our work and in our play,**
Jesus, ever with us stay;
may we serve You all our days,
true and faithful in our ways.

2 May we in Your strength subdue
   evil tempers, words untrue,
   thoughts impure and deeds unkind,
   all things hateful to Your mind.

3 Jesus, from Your throne above,
   fill anew our hearts with love;
   so that what we say and do
   shows that we belong to You.

4 Children of the King are we,
   may we loyal to Him be:
   try to please Him every day,
   in our work and in our play.

111 Anon
Copyright control

In the name of Jesus,
in the name of Jesus,
we have the victory.
In the name of Jesus,
in the name of Jesus,
demons will have to flee.
Who can tell what God can do?
Who can tell of His love for you?
In the name of Jesus, Jesus,
we have the victory.

109 Gordon Brattle (1917–91)
© N A M Cooke

In my need Jesus found me,
put His strong arm around me,
brought me safe home,
into the shelter of the fold.

Gracious shepherd that sought me,
precious life-blood that bought me;
out of the night,
into the light and near to God.

112 Ralph Carmichael
© 1964 Bud John Songs / Alliance Media Ltd /
CopyCare Ltd

In the stars His handiwork I see,
on the wind He speaks with majesty;
though He's ruling over land and sea,
what is that to me?
I will celebrate nativity,
for it has a place in history,
sure, Christ came to set His people free.
What is that to me?

Then by faith I met Him face to face,
and I felt the wonder of His grace.
Then I knew that He was more
        than just a god
who didn't care, who lived away up there.
And now He lives within me day by day,
ever watching o'er me lest I stray,
helping me to find the narrow way.
He's everything to me.

110 From a Polish carol
tr. E M G Reed (1885–1933)
Copyright control

1 **Infant holy, infant lowly,**
   for His bed a cattle stall;
   oxen lowing, little knowing
   Christ the babe is Lord of all.
   Swift are winging angels singing,
   nowells ringing, tidings bringing:
   Christ the babe is Lord of all;
   Christ the babe is Lord of all!

2 Flocks were sleeping, shepherds keeping
   vigil till the morning new,
   saw the glory, heard the story –
   tidings of a gospel true.
   Thus rejoicing, free from sorrow,
   praises voicing, greet the morrow:
   Christ the babe was born for you;
   Christ the babe was born for you!

113 Alfred Henry Ackley (1887–1960)
© 1933, 1961 The Rodeheaver Co / Word Music Inc /
Word Music (UK) / CopyCare Ltd

1 **I serve a risen Saviour,**
   He's in the world today;
   I know that He is living,
   whatever men may say.
   I see His hand of mercy,
   I hear His voice of cheer;
   and just the time I need Him,
   He's always near.

He lives, He lives,
Christ Jesus lives today!
He walks with me and talks with me
along life's narrow way.
He lives, He lives,
salvation to impart!
You ask me how I know He lives?
He lives within my heart.

2   In all the world around me
I see His loving care,
and though my heart grows weary
I never will despair;
I know that He is leading,
through all the stormy blast,
the day of His appearing
will come at last.
He lives . . .

3   Rejoice, rejoice, O Christian,
lift up your voice and sing
eternal hallelujahs
to Jesus Christ the King!
The hope of all who seek Him,
the help of all who find,
none other is so loving,
so good and kind.
He lives . . .

114

Isaiah heard the voice of the Lord
and he said, 'Here am I, send me!'
He loved to do the will of the Lord,
so he said, 'Here am I, send me;
here am I, send me anywhere for Thee.'
So when I hear the voice of the Lord
I will say, 'Here am I, send me!'

115

I sing a song of the saints of God,
patient and brave and true,
who toiled and fought and lived and died
for the Lord they loved and knew.
And one was a doctor,
    and one was a queen,
and one was a shepherdess on the green:
they were all of them saints of God;
    and I mean,
God helping, to be one too.

2   They loved their God so good and dear,
and His love made them strong;
and they followed the right, for Jesus' sake,
the whole of their good lives long.
And one was a soldier, and one was a priest,
and one was slain by a fierce wild beast:
and there's not any reason, no,
    not in the least,
why I shouldn't be one too.

3   They lived not only in ages past,
there are hundreds of thousands still;
the world is bright with the joyous saints
who love to do Jesus' will.
You can meet them in school,
    or in lanes, or at sea,
in church, or in trains, or in shops, or at tea,
for the saints of God began just like me,
and I mean to be one too.

116

1   **It came upon the midnight clear,**
that glorious song of old,
from angels bending near the earth
to touch their harps of gold:
'Peace on the earth, goodwill to men
from heaven's all-gracious King!'
The world in solemn stillness lay
to hear the angels sing.

2   With sorrow brought by sin and strife
the world has suffered long,
and, since the angels sang, have passed
two thousand years of wrong;
for man at war with man hears not
the love-song which they bring:
O hush the noise, you men of strife,
and hear the angels sing!

3   And those whose journey now is hard,
whose hope is burning low,
who tread the rocky path of life
with painful steps and slow:
O listen to the news of love
which makes the heavens ring!
O rest beside the weary road
and hear the angels sing!

4 And still the days are hastening on –
   by prophets seen of old –
   towards the fulness of the time
   when comes the age foretold:
   then earth and heaven renewed shall see
   the Prince of peace, their King;
   and all the world repeat the song
   which now the angels sing.

117 William Walsham How (1823–97)
© in this version Jubilate Hymns

1 **It is a thing most wonderful,**
   almost too wonderful to be,
   that God's own Son
        should come from heaven
   and die to save a child like me.

2 And yet I know that it is true;
   He came to this poor world below
   and wept, and toiled, and mourned,
        and died,
   only because He loved us so.

3 I cannot tell how He could love
   a child so weak and full of sin;
   His love must be so wonderful,
   if He could die my love to win.

4 I sometimes think about the cross,
   and shut my eyes and try to see
   the cruel nails and crown of thorns,
   and Jesus crucified for me.

5 But even could I see Him die,
   I could but see a little part
   of that great love, which, like a fire,
   is always burning in His heart.

6 How wonderful it is to know
   His love for me so free and sure;
   but yet more wonderful to see
   my love for Him so faint and poor.

7 And yet I want to love You, Lord;
   O teach me how to grow in grace,
   that I may love You more and more,
   until I see You face to face.

118 Gary Pfeiffer
© 1973 Fred Bock Music Co /
Kingsway's Thankyou Music

1 **It's a happy day and I praise God**
   for the weather.
   It's a happy day, living it for my Lord.
   It's a happy day, things are going
        to get better,
   living each day by the promises
        in God's word.

2 It's a grumpy day and I can't stand
        the weather.
   It's a grumpy day, living it for myself.
   It's a grumpy day and things aren't going
        to get better,
   living each day with my Bible up on my shelf.

3 It's a happy day and I praise God
        for the weather.
   It's a happy day, living it for my Lord.
   It's a happy day, things are going
        to get better,
   living each day by the promises
        in God's word.

119 Traditional

   It's me, it's me, it's me, O Lord,
   standin' in the need of prayer.
   It's me, it's me, it's me, O Lord,
   standin' in the need of prayer.

1 Not my brother or my sister,
        but it's me, O Lord,
   standin' in the need of prayer.
   Not my brother or my sister,
        but it's me, O Lord,
   standin' in the need of prayer.
   It's me, it's me . . .

2 Not my mother or my father,
        but it's me, O Lord,
   standin' in the need of prayer.
   Not my mother or my father,
        but it's me, O Lord,
   standin' in the need of prayer.
   It's me, it's me . . .

3 Not my stranger or my neighbour,
        but it's me, O Lord,
   standin' in the need of prayer.
   Not my stranger or my neighbour,
        but it's me, O Lord,
   standin' in the need of prayer.
   It's me, it's me . . .

120 Spiritual

   I've got peace like a river,
   peace like a river,
   I've got peace like a river in my soul;
   I've got peace like a river, peace like a river,
   I've got peace like a river in my soul.

121 George W Cooke
Copyright control

I've got that joy, joy, joy, joy
down in my heart, (where?)
down in my heart, (where?)
down in my heart.
I've got that joy, joy, joy, joy
down in my heart, (where?)
down in my heart to stay.
And I'm so happy,
so very happy,
I've got the love of Jesus in my heart,
and I'm so happy,
so very happy,
I've got the love of Jesus in my heart.

I've got the peace
    that passes understanding
down in my heart, (where?)
down in my heart, (where?)
down in my heart.
I've got the peace
    that passes understanding
down in my heart, (where?)
down in my heart to stay.
And I'm so happy . . .

22 Anon
Copyright control

I want to live for Jesus every day
    (every day).
I want to live for Jesus, come what may
    (come what may).
Take the world and all its pleasure,
I've got a more enduring treasure.
I want to live for Jesus every day.

I'm gonna live for Jesus every day
    (every day).
I'm gonna live for Jesus, come what may
    (come what may).
Take the world and all its pleasure,
I've got a more enduring treasure.
I'm gonna live for Jesus every day.

23 Harry D Clarke
© 1927, 1955 Hope Publishing /
CopyCare Ltd

I will make you fishers of men,
fishers of men, fishers of men,
I will make you fishers of men
if you follow Me.
If you follow Me, if you follow Me,
I will make you fishers of men
if you follow Me.

124 © 1964 C Simmonds

1 I want to walk with Jesus Christ,
    all the days I live of this life on earth;
    to give to Him complete control
    of body and of soul.
    Follow Him, follow Him,
    yield your life to Him –
    He has conquered death,
    He is King of kings;
    accept the joy which He gives to those
    who yield their lives to Him.

2 I want to learn to speak to Him,
    to pray to Him, confess my sin,
    to open my life and let Him in,
    for joy will then be mine.
    Follow Him, follow Him . . .

3 I want to learn to speak of Him –
    my life must show that He lives in me;
    my deeds, my thoughts, my words
        must speak
    all of His love for me.
    Follow Him, follow Him . . .

4 I want to learn to read His word,
    for this is how I know the way
    to live my life as pleases Him,
    in holiness and joy.
    Follow Him, follow Him . . .

5 O Holy Spirit of the Lord,
    enter now into this heart of mine;
    take full control of my selfish will
    and make me wholly Thine!
    Follow Him, follow Him . . .

125 Anon
Copyright control

1 I was lost but Jesus found me,
    found the sheep that went astray,
    threw His loving arms around me,
    drew me back into His way.
    Alleluia, alleluia,
    alleluia, alleluia.

2 Glory, glory, alleluia,
    come and bless the Lord our King.
    Glory, glory, alleluia,
    with His praise all heaven rings.
    Alleluia . . .

126
Max Dyer
© 1975 Celebration /
Kingsway's Thankyou Music

1 **I will sing, I will sing a song
unto the Lord,** (*3 times*)
alleluia, glory to the Lord.
*Allelu, alleluia, glory to the Lord,
allelu, alleluia, glory to the Lord,
allelu, alleluia, glory to the Lord,
alleluia, glory to the Lord.*

2 We will come, we will come as one
before the Lord, (*3 times*)
alleluia, glory to the Lord.
Allelu, alleluia . . .

3 If the Son, if the Son shall make you free,
(*3 times*)
you shall be free indeed.
Allelu, alleluia . . .

4 They that sow in tears shall reap in joy,
(*3 times*)
alleluia, glory to the Lord!
Allelu, alleluia . . .

5 Every knee shall bow and every
tongue confess, (*3 times*)
that Jesus Christ is Lord.
Allelu, alleluia . . .

6 In His name, in His name we have
the victory. (*3 times*)
Alleluia, glory to the Lord.
Allelu, alleluia . . .

127
Francis Harold Rawley (1854–1952)
© HarperCollins*Religious* / CopyCare Ltd

1 **I will sing the wondrous story**
of the Christ who died for me –
how He left the realms of glory
for the cross on Calvary.
Yes, I'll sing the wondrous story
of the Christ who died for me –
sing it with His saints in glory,
gathered by the crystal sea.

2 I was lost: but Jesus found me,
found the sheep that went astray,
raised me up and gently led me
back into the narrow way.
Days of darkness still may meet me,
sorrow's path I oft may tread;
but His presence still is with me,
by His guiding hand I'm led.

3 He will keep me till the river
rolls its waters at my feet:
then He'll bear me safely over,
made by grace for glory meet.
Yes, I'll sing the wondrous story
of the Christ who died for me –
sing it with His saints in glory,
gathered by the crystal sea.

128
Susan Warner (1819–85)

1 **Jesus bids us shine**
with a pure, clear light,
like a little candle
burning in the night.
In this world is darkness,
so let us shine,
you in your small corner
and I in mine.

2 Jesus bids us shine
first of all for Him.
Well He sees and knows it,
if our light grows dim.
He looks down from heaven
to see us shine,
you in your small corner
and I in mine.

3 Jesus bids us shine, then,
for all around;
many kinds of darkness
in the world are found –
sin and want and sorrow –
so we must shine,
you in your small corner
and I in mine.

129
Anon
Copyright control

Jesus Christ is alive today,
I know, I know it's true.
Sovereign of the universe,
I give Him homage due.
Seated there at God's right hand,
I am with Him in the promised land.
Jesus lives and reigns in me,
that's how I know it's true.

130 *Lyra Davidica, 1708*

1 **Jesus Christ is risen today,** *hallelujah!*
our triumphant holy day, *hallelujah!*
who did once upon the cross, *hallelujah!*
suffer to redeem our loss, *hallelujah!*

2 Hymns of praise then let us sing, *hallelujah!*
unto Christ our heavenly King, *hallelujah!*
who endured the cross and grave,
    hallelujah!
sinners to redeem and save, *hallelujah!*

3 But the pains which He endured, *hallelujah!*
our salvation have procured, *hallelujah!*
now in heaven above He's King, *hallelujah!*
Where the angels ever sing, *'hallelujah!'*

131 From the German (15th century)
Michael Perry (1942–1996)
© Executors of the late Michael Perry / Jubilate Hymns

Jesus Christ the Lord is born,
all the bells are ringing!
Angels greet the Holy One
and shepherds hear them singing,
and shepherds hear them singing.

'Go to Bethlehem today,
find your King and Saviour:
glory be to God on high,
to earth His peace and favour,
to earth His peace and favour!'

Held within a cattle stall,
loved by love maternal,
see the Master of us all,
our Lord of lords eternal,
our Lord of lords eternal!

Soon shall come the wise men three,
rousing Herod's anger;
mothers' hearts shall broken be
and Mary's Son in danger,
and Mary's Son in danger.

Death from life and life from death,
our salvation story;
let all living things give breath
to Christmas songs of glory,
to Christmas songs of glory!

132 Anon
Copyright control

Jesus died for all the children,
all the children of the world.
Red and yellow, black and white,
all are precious in His sight:
Jesus died for all the children of the world.

133 David Bolton
© 1975 Kingsway's Thankyou Music

Jesus, how lovely You are!
You are so gentle, so pure and kind,
You shine like the morning star:
Jesus, how lovely You are.

1 Alleluia, Jesus is my Lord and King;
alleluia, Jesus is my everything.
Jesus, how lovely . . .

2 Alleluia, Jesus died and rose again;
alleluia, Jesus forgave all my sin.
Jesus, how lovely . . .

3 Alleluia, Jesus is meek and lowly;
alleluia, Jesus is pure and holy.
Jesus, how lovely . . .

4 Alleluia, Jesus is the bridegroom;
alleluia, Jesus will take His bride soon.
Jesus, how lovely . . .

134 Margaret Cropper
© Stainer & Bell Ltd

1 **Jesus' hands were kind hands,**
doing good to all,
healing pain and sickness,
blessing children small,
washing tired feet
and saving those who fall;
Jesus' hands were kind hands
doing good to all.

2 Take my hands, Lord Jesus,
let them work for You,
make them strong and gentle,
kind in all I do.
Let me watch You, Jesus,
till I'm gentle too,
till my hands are kind hands,
quick to work for You.

135 Gordon Brattle (1917–91)
© N A M Cooke

Jesus is knocking, patiently waiting,
outside your heart's closed door.
Do not reject Him, simply accept Him,
now and for evermore.

136 Paul Mazak
© 1974, 1975 Celebration / Kingsway's Thankyou Music

1 **Jesus is a friend of mine,**
praise Him!
Jesus is a friend of mine,
praise Him!
Praise Him! Praise Him!
Jesus is a friend of mine,
praise Him!

2 Jesus died to set us free,
praise Him!
Jesus died to set us free,
praise Him!
Praise Him! Praise Him!
Jesus died to set us free,
praise Him!

3 Jesus is the King of kings,
praise Him!
Jesus is the King of kings,
praise Him!
Praise Him! Praise Him!
Jesus is the King of kings,
praise Him!

137 David J Mansell
© 1982 Springtide / Word Music (UK) /
CopyCare Ltd

1 **Jesus is Lord!**
Creation's voice proclaims it,
for by His power each tree and flower
was planned and made.
Jesus is Lord! The universe declares it;
sun, moon and stars in heaven cry:
'Jesus is Lord!'
Jesus is Lord! Jesus is Lord!
Praise Him with hallelujahs,
for Jesus is Lord!

2 Jesus is Lord! Yet from His throne eternal
in flesh He came to die in pain
on Calvary's tree.

Jesus is Lord! From Him all life proceeding,
yet gave His life a ransom
thus setting us free.
Jesus is Lord . . .

3 Jesus is Lord! O'er sin the mighty conqueror,
from death He rose and all His foes
shall own His name.
Jesus is Lord! God sends His Holy Spirit
to show by works of power
that Jesus is Lord.
Jesus is Lord . . .

138 © 1971 Roger Jones /
National Council of Christian Education

Jesus, I will come with You,
I will follow in Your way.
I will trust You,
I will bring You all I have today.
Jesus, You're the way,
Jesus, You're the truth,
Jesus, You're the life,
praise Your name.

139 H W Rattle
© Scripture Union

Jesus' love is very wonderful,
Jesus' love is very wonderful,
Jesus' love is very wonderful,
O wonderful love!
So high you can't get over it,
so low you can't get under it,
so wide you can't get round it,
O wonderful love!

140 Anna Warner (1827–1915)

1 **Jesus loves me! this I know,**
for the Bible tells me so.
Little ones to Him belong;
they are weak, but He is strong.
Yes, Jesus loves me!
Yes, Jesus loves me!
Yes, Jesus loves me!
The Bible tells me so.

2 Jesus loves me! He who died,
heaven's gate to open wide;
He will wash away my sin,
let His little child come in.
Yes, Jesus loves me . . .

Jesus loves me! He will stay
close beside me all the way;
then His little child will take
up to heaven, for His dear sake.
Yes, Jesus loves me . . .

41
Naida Hearn
© 1974 Scripture in Song /
Integrity's Hosanna! Music /
Kingsway's Thankyou Music

Jesus, name above all names,
beautiful Saviour, glorious Lord;
Emmanuel, God is with us,
blessèd Redeemer, living Word.

42
Anon
Copyright control

Jesus said that whosoever will,
whosoever will, whosoever will,
Jesus said that whosoever will,
whosoever will may come.

I'm so glad that He included me,
He included me, He included me,
I'm so glad that He included me,
when Jesus said that whosoever
    will may come.

43
Spiritual

Joshua fit the battle of Jericho,
Jericho, Jericho,
Joshua fit the battle of Jericho
and the walls came tumbling down.

You may talk about your king of Gideon,
you may talk about your man of Saul,
but there's none like good old Joshua
at the battle of Jericho.

Up to the walls of Jericho
he marched with spear in hand.
'Go, blow them ram-horns,' Joshua cried,
''cause the battle am in my hand!'

Then the ram-sheep's horns began to blow,
trumpets began to sound.
Joshua commanded the children to shout
and the walls came tumbling
    down that morning.
Joshua fit the battle . . .

144
Anon
Copyright control

Joy is the flag flown high from the castle
  of my heart,
from the castle of my heart,
from the castle of my heart,
joy is the flag flown high from the castle
  of my heart
when the King is in residence there.
  So let it fly in the sky,
    let the whole world know,
  let the whole world know,
  let the whole world know,
  so let it fly in the sky,
    let the whole world know
that the King is in residence there.

145
From Psalm 100, Fred Dunn (1909–79)
© 1977, 1980 Kingsway's Thankyou Music

Jubilate, everybody,
serve the Lord in all your ways, and
come before His presence singing:
enter now His courts with praise.
For the Lord our God is gracious,
and His mercy everlasting.
Jubilate, jubilate,
jubilate Deo!

146
Marianne Farningham (1834–1909)
altered © 1986 Horrobin / Leavers

1 **Just as I am, Your child to be,**
friend of the young, who died for me,
to give my life wholeheartedly,
O Jesus Christ, I come.

2 While I am still a child today,
I give my life, my work and play
to Him alone, without delay,
with all my heart I come.

3 I see in Jesus Christ the light,
with Him as Lord, and in His might
I turn from sin to what is right,
My Lord, to You I come.

4 Lord, take my dreams of fame and gold,
I accept now a life controlled
by faith in You, as days unfold,
with my whole life I come.

5 Just as I am, young, strong and free,
  to be the best that I can be,
  that others may see You in me,
  Lord of my life, I come.

147 Kate Barclay Wilkinson (1858–1928)
Copyright control

Keep me shining, Lord,
keep me shining, Lord,
in all I say or do,
that the world may see
Christ lives in me,
and learn to love Him too.

148 Sophie Conty and Naomi Batya
© 1980 Maranatha! Music /
CopyCare Ltd

King of kings and Lord of lords,
  glory, hallelujah!
King of kings and Lord of lords,
  glory, hallelujah!
Jesus, Prince of peace,
  glory, hallelujah!
Jesus, Prince of peace,
  glory, hallelujah!

149 Traditional

1 **Kum ba yah, my Lord, kum ba yah,**
  kum ba yah, my Lord, kum ba yah,
  kum ba yah, my Lord, kum ba yah,
  O Lord, kum ba yah.

2 Someone's crying, Lord . . .

3 Someone's singing, Lord . . .

4 Someone's praying, Lord . . .

5 Hear our prayer, O Lord, hear our prayer.
  Keep our friends, O Lord, in Your care,
  keep our friends, O Lord, in Your care,
  O Lord, kum ba yah.

150 H Buffum Jr
Copyright control

Let's talk about Jesus,
    the King of kings is He,
  the Lord of lords, supreme
    through all eternity,
  the great I AM, the way, the truth,
    the life, the door.
  Let's talk about Jesus, more and more.

151 Graham Kendrick
© 1983 Kingsway's Thankyou Music

1 **Led like a lamb to the slaughter,**
  in silence and shame,
  there on Your back You carried a world
  of violence and pain.
  Bleeding, dying, bleeding, dying.
    You're alive,
    You're alive,
    You have risen!
    Alleluia!
    And the power
    and the glory
    is given,
    Alleluia!
    Jesus, to You.

2 At break of dawn, poor Mary,
  still weeping she came,
  when through her grief
  she heard Your voice,
  now speaking her name.
  Mary! Master! Mary! Master!
    You're alive . . .

3 At the right hand of the Father,
  now seated on high,
  You have begun Your eternal reign
  of justice and joy.
  Glory, glory, glory, glory.
    You're alive . . .

152 James E Seddon (1915–83)
© 1969 Mavis Seddon / Jubilate Hymns

1 **Let us praise God together,**
  let us praise.
  Let us praise God together,
  Him proclaim.
  He is faithful in all His ways,
  He is worthy of all our praise,
  His name be exalted on high.

2 Let us seek God together,
let us pray.
Let us seek His forgiveness
as we pray.
He will cleanse us from all sin,
He will help us the fight to win,
His name be exalted on high.

3 Let us serve God together,
let us serve.
Let our lives show His goodness
as we work.
Christ the Lord is the world's true light,
let us serve Him with all our might.
His name be exalted on high.

153 © Marcus Uzilevsky / Oaksprings Impressions

Live, live, live,
live, live, live,
Jesus is living in my soul.
Live, live, live,
live, live, live,
Jesus is living in my soul.

Hanging on the tree
He prayed for you and me.
Jesus is living in my soul.
To His spirit yield –
by His stripes we're healed.
Jesus is living in my soul.
Live, live, live . . .

He took me out of darkness
and He set me free.
Jesus is living in my soul.
Once I was blind,
now I can see.
Jesus is living in my soul.
Live, live, live . . .

Gonna shout and sing,
let the hallelujah ring.
Jesus is living in my soul.
I'm gonna shout and sing,
there's healing in His wing.
Jesus is living in my soul.
Live, live, live . . .

154 John Milton (1608–74)

Let us with a gladsome mind
praise the Lord for He is kind;

For His mercies still endure,
ever faithful, ever sure.

2 He, with all-commanding might,
filled the new-made world with light:
For His mercies . . .

3 All things living He does feed,
His full hand supplies their need:
For His mercies . . .

4 Let us then with gladsome mind,
praise the Lord for He is kind!
For His mercies . . .

155 John Fawcett (1740–1817)
altered © 1986 Horrobin / Leavers

1 **Lord, dismiss us with Your blessing,**
fill our hearts with joy and peace.
Let us each, Your love possessing,
triumph in redeeming grace.
O refresh us, O refresh us
as to serve we leave this place.

2 Thanks we give and adoration
for Your gospel's joyful sound;
may the fruits of Your salvation
in our hearts and lives abound;
so Your presence, so Your presence
will with us be always found.

156 Patrick Appleford
© 1960 Josef Weinberger Ltd

1 **Lord Jesus Christ, You have come to us,**
You are one with us, Mary's Son;
cleansing our souls from all their sin,
pouring Your love and goodness in:
Jesus, our love for You we sing –
living Lord!

2 Lord Jesus Christ, now and every day
teach us how to pray, Son of God;
You have commanded us to do
this in remembrance, Lord, of You:
into our lives Your power breaks through –
living Lord!

3 Lord Jesus Christ, You have come to us,
born as one of us, Mary's Son;
led out to die on Calvary,
risen from death to set us free:
living Lord Jesus, help us see
You are Lord!

4 Lord Jesus Christ, I would come to You,
live my life for You, Son of God;
all Your commands I know are true,
Your many gifts will make me new:
into my life Your power breaks through –
living Lord!

157

Jan Struther (1901–53)
From Enlarged Songs of Praise
by permission of Oxford University Press

1 **Lord of all hopefulness, Lord of all joy,**
whose trust, ever childlike,
no cares could destroy,
be there at our waking, and give us, we pray,
Your bliss in our hearts, Lord,
at the break of the day.

2 Lord of all eagerness, Lord of all faith,
whose strong hands were skilled
at the plane and the lathe,
be there at our labours,
and give us, we pray,
Your strength in our hearts, Lord,
at the noon of the day.

3 Lord of all kindliness, Lord of all grace,
Your hand swift to welcome,
Your arms to embrace,
be there at our homing,
and give us, we pray,
Your love in our hearts, Lord,
at the eve of the day.

4 Lord of all gentleness, Lord of all calm,
whose voice is contentment,
whose presence is balm,
be there at our sleeping,
and give us, we pray,
Your peace in our hearts, Lord,
at the end of the day.

158

© 1986 Andy Silver

Love, joy, peace and patience, kindness,
goodness, meekness, faith, self-control.
These are the fruit of God's Holy Spirit
and against such there is no law.
Those who belong to Christ should now
live this way,
walking in the Spirit each day,
so praise Him, praise Him,
give Him all the glory,
walking in the Spirit each day.

159

Robert Lowry (1826–99)

1 **Low in the grave He lay,**
Jesus, my Saviour;
waiting the coming day,
Jesus, my Lord.
Up from the grave He arose,
with a mighty triumph o'er His foes;
He arose a victor from the dark domain,
and He lives for ever
with His saints to reign:
He arose! He arose! Hallelujah!
Christ arose!

2 Vainly they watch His bed,
Jesus, my Saviour;
vainly they seal the dead,
Jesus, my Lord.
Up from the grave . . .

3 Death cannot keep his prey,
Jesus, my Saviour,
He tore the bars away,
Jesus, my Lord.
Up from the grave . . .

160

Jack Hayford
© 1981 Rocksmith Music /
Leosong Copyright Services Ltd

Majesty, worship His majesty;
unto Jesus be glory, honour and praise.
Majesty, kingdom authority,
flows from His throne
unto His own, His anthem raise.
So exalt, lift up on high the name of Jesus,
magnify, come, glorify Christ Jesus the King.
Majesty, worship His majesty,
Jesus who died, now glorified,
King of all kings.

161

Sebastian Temple
© 1967 Franciscan Communications

1 **Make me a channel of Your peace.**
Where there is hatred let me bring Your love
where there is injury, Your pardon, Lord;
and where there's doubt, true faith in You.
O Master, grant that I may never seek
so much to be consoled as to console;
to be understood as to understand;
to be loved, as to love with all my soul.

2 Make me a channel of Your peace.
Where there's despair in life
let me bring hope;
where there is darkness, only light;
and where there's sadness, ever joy.
O Master . . .

3 Make me a channel of Your peace.
It is in pardoning that we are pardoned,
in giving to all men that we receive;
and in dying that we're born to eternal life.

162 Kelly Willard
© 1982 Maranatha! Music / CopyCare Ltd

Make me a servant, humble and meek.
Lord, let me lift up those who are weak.
And may the prayer of my heart always be:
'Make me a servant, make me a servant,
make me a servant today.'

163 R Hudson Pope (1879–1967)
© Scripture Gift Mission

Make the book live to me, O Lord,
show me Yourself within Your word,
show me myself and show me my Saviour
and make the book live to me.

164 © 1986 Andy Silver

Mary had a little baby,
Mary had a little baby;
here and there and everywhere
the angels sang:
'Praise the Lord!'
Mary had a little baby, Mary had a little baby;
here and there and everywhere
the angels sang:
'Praise the Lord!'

Glory, glory, glory, glory,
everybody sing the song.
Glory, glory, glory, glory,
God's Son has come to earth.

Mary had a little baby, Mary had a little baby;
here and there and everywhere
the angels sang:
'Praise the Lord!'

165 Kate Barclay Wilkinson (1859–1928)
Copyright control

1 **May the mind of Christ my Saviour**
live in me from day to day,
by His love and power controlling
all I do or say.

2 May the word of God dwell richly
in my heart from hour to hour,
so that all may see I triumph
only through His power.

3 May the peace of God my Father
rule my life in everything,
that I may be calm to comfort
sick and sorrowing.

4 May the love of Jesus fill me,
as the waters fill the sea;
Him uplifting, self denying,
this is victory.

5 May I run the race before me,
strong and brave onward I go,
looking only unto Jesus,
as in Him I grow.

166 Eleanor Farjeon (1881–1965)
© David Higham Associates Ltd
from *The Children's Bells*
published by Oxford University Press

1 **Morning has broken**
like the first morning;
blackbird has spoken
like the first bird.
Praise for the singing!
Praise for the morning!
Praise for them, springing
fresh from the Word!

2 Mine is the sunlight!
Mine is the morning,
here in the bright light
of this fair day!
Praise with elation,
praise every morning
God's re-creation
of the new day!

167 Anon
Copyright control

1 **Mister Noah built an ark,**
the people thought it such a lark.
Mister Noah pleaded so,
but into the ark they would not go.

*Down came the rain in torrents
(splish, splash),
down came the rain in torrents
(splish, splash),
down came the rain in torrents,
and only eight were saved.*

2 The animals went in two by two,
elephant, giraffe and kangaroo.
All were safely stowed away
on that great and awful day.
Down came the rain . . .

*Whenever you see a rainbow,
whenever you see a rainbow,
whenever you see a rainbow,
remember God is love.*

 168 Thomas Toke Lynch (1818–71)
altered © 1986 Horrobin / Leavers

1 **My faith is like a staff of oak,**
the traveller's well-loved aid;
my faith, it is a weapon strong,
the soldier's trusty blade.
I'll travel on, and still be stirred
to action at my Master's word;
by all life's perils undeterred,
a soldier unafraid.

2 My faith is like a staff of oak,
O let me on it lean!
My faith, it is a sharpened sword,
may falsehood find it keen!
Now fill me with Your Spirit, Lord,
teach and change me through Your word,
and by Your love may I be stirred,
as all true saints have been.

169 Anon
Copyright control

1 **My God is so big, so strong
and so mighty**
there's nothing that He cannot do.
My God is so big, so strong and so mighty
there's nothing that He cannot do.
The rivers are His, the mountains are His,
the stars are His handiwork too.
My God is so big, so strong and so mighty
there's nothing that He cannot do.

2 My God is so big, so strong and so mighty
there's nothing that He cannot do.
My God is so big, so strong and so mighty
there's nothing that He cannot do.
He's called you to live for Him every day
in all that you say and you do.
My God is so big, so strong and so mighty,
He can do all things through you.

170 Ian Smale
© 1981 Kingsway's Thankyou Music

My Lord is higher than a mountain,
He is stronger than an army,
He is wiser than any man can tell.
My Lord is faster than a rocket,
can see more than a telescope,
is bigger than the universe as well.
His love is warmer than the burning sun,
closer than the nearest friend,
more real than any truth can be.
My Lord, He knows about the past,
and He knows about the future,
and He also knows all about me.

171 John Keble (1792–1866)

1 **New every morning is the love**
our waking and uprising prove:
through sleep and darkness safely brought,
restored to life and power and thought.

2 New mercies, each returning day,
surround Your people as they pray:
new dangers past, new sins forgiven,
new thoughts of God, new hopes of heaven.

3 If in our daily life our mind
be set to honour all we find,
new treasures still, of countless price,
God will provide for sacrifice.

4 The trivial round, the common task,
will give us all we ought to ask:
room to deny ourselves, a road
to bring us daily nearer God.

5 Prepare us, Lord, in Your dear love
for perfect rest with You above,
and help us, this and every day,
to grow more like You as we pray.

172
J H Cansdale (d 1995)
© Michael Cansdale
altered 1985 Horrobin / Leavers

Now be strong and very courageous,
for I have commanded you.
Be not afraid,
be not dismayed;
you will have victory.
I will be with you unto the end,
captain and leader,
guide and friend.

173
Sabine Baring-Gould (1834–1924)
altered © 1986 Horrobin / Leavers

Now the day is over,
night will soon be here,
help me to remember
You are always near.

As the darkness gathers,
stars shine overhead,
creatures, birds and flowers
rest their weary heads.

Father, give all people
calm and peaceful rest;
through Your gracious presence
may our sleep be blessed.

Comfort every sufferer
watching late in pain;
those who plan some evil
from their sin restrain.

When the morning wakes me,
ready for the day,
help me, Lord, to serve You,
walking in Your way.

Glory to the Father,
glory to the Son,
and to the Holy Spirit,
blessing everyone.

174
J M C Crum (1872–1958)
From the *Oxford Book of Carols*
by permission of Oxford University Press

Now the green blade riseth
   from the buried grain,
wheat that in the dark earth
   many days has lain.
Love lives again,
   that with the dead has been.
Love is come again,
   like wheat that springeth green.

2 In the grave they laid Him,
      Love whom men had slain,
   thinking that never He would wake again.
   Laid in the earth like grain
      that sleeps unseen,
   Love is come again,
      like wheat that springeth green.

3 Forth He came at Easter, like the risen grain,
   He that for three days in the grave had lain.
   Quick from the dead my risen Lord is seen;
   Love is come again,
      like wheat that springeth green.

4 When our hearts are wintry,
      grieving or in pain,
   Your touch can call us back to life again.
   Fields of our hearts
      that dead and bare have been;
   Love is come again,
      like wheat that springeth green.

175
Martin Rinkart (1586–1649)
tr. Catherine Winkworth (1829–78)
altered © 1986 Horrobin / Leavers

1 **Now thank we all our God,**
   with hearts, and hands, and voices;
   who wondrous things has done,
   in whom His world rejoices;
   who, from our mothers' arms,
   has blessed us on our way
   with countless gifts of love,
   and still is ours today.

2 We thank You, then, O God
   that through our life You're near us,
   for joy that fills our hearts,
   which, with Your peace, restores us.
   Lord, keep us in Your grace,
   and guide us when perplexed,
   that we may love Your ways,
   in this world and the next.

3 All praise and thanks to God
   the Father now be given,
   the Son, and Him who reigns
   with Them in highest heaven;
   the one eternal God,
   whom earth and heaven adore;
   for thus it was, is now,
   and shall be evermore.

176
From the Latin (18th century)
tr. Frederick Oakley (1802–80)
altered © 1986 Horrobin / Leavers

1 **O come, all you faithful,**
joyful and triumphant,
O come now, O come now to Bethlehem;
come and behold Him,
born the King of angels:
O come, let us adore Him,
O come, let us adore Him,
O come, let us adore Him,
Christ the Lord!

2 True God of true God,
light of light eternal,
He, who abhors not the virgin's womb;
Son of the Father,
begotten not created:
O come, let us adore Him . . .

3 Sing like the angels,
sing in exultation,
sing with the citizens of heaven above,
'Glory to God,
glory in the highest':
O come, let us adore Him . . .

4 Yes, Lord, we greet You,
born that happy morning,
Jesus, to You be glory given!
Word of the Father,
then in flesh appearing:
O come, let us adore Him . . .

177
From the Latin (12th century)
tr. John Mason Neale (1818–66)
© in this version Jubilate Hymns

1 **O come, O come, Emmanuel,**
and ransom captive Israel,
who mourns in lonely exile here
until the Son of God draws near.
Rejoice, rejoice! Emmanuel
shall come to you, O Israel.

2 O come, true Branch of Jesse, free
Your children from this tyranny;
from depths of hell Your people save,
to rise victorious from the grave.
Rejoice, rejoice . . .

3 O come, bright Daybreak, come and cheer
our spirits by Your advent here;
dispel the long night's lingering gloom
and pierce the shadows of the tomb.
Rejoice, rejoice . . .

4 O come, strong key of David, come
and open wide our heavenly home;
make safe the path that leads on high,
and close the path to misery.
Rejoice, rejoice . . .

5 O come, O come, great Lord of might,
who long ago on Sinai's height
gave all Your tribes the ancient law
in cloud and majesty and awe.
Rejoice, rejoice . . .

178
Philip Dodderidge (1702–51)
altered © 1986 Horrobin / Leavers

1 **O happy day! that fixed my choice**
on You, my Saviour and my God!
Well may this grateful heart rejoice,
and tell of Christ's redeeming blood.
O happy day! O happy day!
when Jesus washed my sins away;
He taught me how to watch and pray,
and live rejoicing every day; (hallelujah!)
O happy day! O happy day!
when Jesus washed my sins away.

2 It's done, the great transaction's done!
I am my Lord's and He is mine!
He led me, and I followed on,
responding to the voice divine.
O happy day . . .

3 Now rest, my long-divided heart,
in Jesus Christ who loves you, rest;
and never from your Lord depart,
enriched by Him, by Him possessed.
O happy day . . .

4 So God, who heard the solemn vow,
in daily prayer shall hear my voice,
till in my final breath I bow,
and bless the day that fixed my choice.
O happy day . . .

179
Russian hymn
tr. Stuart Wesley Keene Hine (1899–1989)
© 1953 Kingsway's Thankyou Music

1 **O Lord my God!**
   when I in awesome wonder
consider all the works Thy hand hath made
I see the stars, I hear the mighty thunder,
the power throughout the universe
   displayed;

Then sings my soul,
my Saviour God, to Thee,
how great Thou art, how great Thou art!
Then sings my soul,
my Saviour God, to Thee,
how great Thou art, how great Thou art!

When through the woods
and forest glades I wander
and hear the birds sing sweetly in the trees;
when I look down
from lofty mountain grandeur,
and hear the brook,
and feel the gentle breeze;
Then sings my soul . . .

And when I think
that God, His Son not sparing,
sent Him to die – I scarce can take it in,
that on the cross my burden gladly bearing,
He bled and died to take away my sin:
Then sings my soul . . .

When Christ shall come
with shout of acclamation
and take me home –
what joy shall fill my heart!
Then shall I bow in humble adoration
and there proclaim,
my God, how great Thou art!
Then sings my soul . . .

80 Anon
Copyright control

O! O! O! how good is the Lord,
O! O! O! how good is the Lord,
O! O! O! how good is the Lord,
I never will forget
what He has done for me.

He gives me salvation,
how good is the Lord,
He gives me salvation,
how good is the Lord,
He gives me salvation,
how good is the Lord,
I never will forget what He has done for me.
O! O! O! . . .

He gives me His blessings . . .
O! O! O! . . .

He gives me His Spirit . . .
O! O! O! . . .

He gives me His healing . . .
O! O! O! . . .

5 He gives me His glory . . .
O! O! O! . . .

OTHER SUITABLE VERSES MAY BE ADDED
He gives us each other . . .
He gives us His body . . .
He gives us His freedom . . . *etc.*

181 William Reed Newell (1868–1956)
Copyright control

O the love that drew salvation's plan!
O the grace that brought it down to man!
O the mighty gulf that God did span
    at Calvary.
Mercy there was great and grace was free,
pardon there was multiplied to me,
there my burdened soul found liberty,
    at Calvary.

182 Phillips Brooks (1835–93)

1 **O little town of Bethlehem,**
how still we see you lie!
Above your deep and dreamless sleep
the silent stars go by:
yet in your dark streets shining
is everlasting light;
the hopes and fears of all the years
are met in you tonight.

2 For Christ is born of Mary;
and, gathered all above,
while mortals sleep, the angels keep
their watch of wondering love.
O morning stars, together
proclaim the holy birth,
and praises sing to God the King,
and peace to men on earth.

3 How silently, how silently,
the wondrous gift is given!
So God imparts to human hearts
the blessings of His heaven.
No ear may hear His coming;
but in this world of sin,
where meek souls will receive Him, still
the dear Christ enters in.

4 O holy Child of Bethlehem,
  descend to us, we pray;
  cast out our sin, and enter in;
  be born in us today.
  We hear the Christmas angels
  the great glad tidings tell;
  O come to us, abide with us,
  our Lord Immanuel.

183 A W Edsor
© Kingsway's Thankyou Music

On Calvary's tree He died for me,
that I His love might know.
To set me free He died for me –
that's why I love Him so.

184 Traditional

1 **Oh, the Lord looked down
   from His window in the sky,**
   said, 'I created man
     but I can't remember why!
   Nothing but fighting since creation day.
   I'll send a little water
     and wash them all away.'
   Oh, the Lord came down and looked
     around a spell.
   There was Mr Noah behaving mighty well.
   And that is the reason, the Scriptures record,
   Noah found grace in the eyes of the Lord.
     Noah found grace in the eyes of the Lord,
     Noah found grace in the eyes of the Lord,
     Noah found grace in the eyes of the Lord,
     and He left him high and dry.

2 The Lord said, 'Noah, there's going
     to be a flood,
   there's going to be some water,
     there's going to be some mud.
   So take off your hat, Noah,
     take off your coat,
   get Shem and Ham and Japheth
     and build yourself a boat.'
   Noah said, 'Lord, I don't believe I could.'
   The Lord said, 'Noah, get yourself
     some wood.
   You never know what you can do till you try.
   Build it fifty cubits wide
     and thirty cubits high.'
     Noah found grace . . .

3 Noah said, 'There she is, there she is, Lord!'
  The Lord said, 'Noah, it's time to get aboard.
  Take of each creature a he and a she,
  and of course take Mrs Noah
    and the whole family.'
  Noah said, 'Lord, it's getting mighty dark.'
  The Lord said, 'Noah, get those creatures
    in the ark.'
  Noah said, 'Lord, it's beginning to pour.'
  The Lord said, 'Noah, hurry up
    and close the door.'
    Noah found grace . . .

4 The ark rose up on the bosom of the deep.
  After forty days Mr Noah took a peep.
  He said, 'We're not moving, Lord,
    where are we at?'
  The Lord said, 'You're sitting right
    on Mount Ararat.'
  Noah said, 'Lord, it's getting nice and dry.'
  The Lord said, 'Noah, see my rainbow
    in the sky.
  Take all your creatures and people the earth,
  and be sure you're not more trouble than
    you're worth.'
    Noah found grace . . .

185 Cecil Frances Alexander (1818–95)

1 **Once in royal David's city,**
  stood a lowly cattle shed,
  where a mother laid her baby,
  in a manger for His bed.
  Mary was that mother mild,
  Jesus Christ her little child.

2 He came down to earth from heaven,
  who is God and Lord of all;
  and His shelter was a stable,
  and His cradle was a stall:
  with the poor and mean and lowly
  lived on earth our Saviour holy.

3 And through all His wondrous childhood
  He would honour and obey,
  love, and watch the lowly mother,
  in whose gentle arms He lay:
  Christian children all should be,
  kind, obedient, good as He.

4 For He is our childhood's pattern:
  day by day like us He grew;
  He was little, weak, and helpless,
  tears and smiles like us He knew;
  and He feels for all our sadness,
  and He shares in all our gladness.

5 And our eyes at last shall see Him,
through His own redeeming love;
for that child, so dear and gentle,
is our Lord in heaven above;
and He leads His children on
to the place where He is gone.

6 Not in that poor lowly stable,
with the oxen standing by,
we shall see Him, but in heaven,
set at God's right hand on high;
there His children gather round,
bright like stars, with glory crowned.

186 Charles Coffin (1676–1749)
tr. John Chandler (1806–76)
altered © 1986 Horrobin / Leavers

1 **On Jordan's bank the Baptist's cry**
announces that the Lord is nigh;
come then and listen for he brings
glad tidings from the King of kings.

2 Then cleansed be every heart from sin;
make straight the way for God within;
prepare we in our hearts a home,
where such a mighty guest may come.

3 For You are our salvation, Lord,
our refuge and our great reward;
without Your grace we waste away,
like flowers that wither and decay.

4 To Him who left the throne of heaven
to save mankind, all praise be given;
to God the Father, voices raise,
and Holy Spirit, let us praise.

187 J Wilbur Chapman (1859–1918)

**One day when heaven was filled
with His praises,**
one day when sin was as black as could be,
Jesus came down to be born of a virgin,
lived among men, my example is He!
Living, He loved me; dying, He saved me;
buried, He carried my sins far away,
rising, He justified freely for ever:
one day He's coming: O glorious day.

One day they led Him
up Calvary's mountain,
one day they nailed Him to die on the tree;
suffering anguish, despised and rejected;
bearing our sins, my Redeemer is He!
Living, He loved me . . .

3 One day they left Him alone in the garden,
one day He rested, from suffering free;
angels came down o'er His tomb
to keep vigil;
hope of the hopeless, my Saviour is He!
Living, He loved me . . .

4 One day the grave could conceal Him
no longer,
one day the stone rolled away from the door;
then He arose,
over death He had conquered;
now is ascended, my Lord evermore!
Living, He loved me . . .

5 One day the trumpet will sound
for His coming,
one day the skies with His glory will shine;
wonderful day, my beloved ones bringing;
glorious Saviour, this Jesus is mine!
Living, He loved me . . .

188 Sydney Carter
© 1971 Stainer & Bell Ltd

1 **One more step along the world I go,**
one more step along the world I go,
from the old things to the new
keep me travelling along with You.
And it's from the old I travel to the new,
keep me travelling along with You.

2 Round the corners of the world I turn,
more and more about the world I learn.
And the new things that I see
You'll be looking at along with me.
And it's from the old . . .

3 As I travel through the bad and good
keep me travelling the way I should.
Where I see no way to go
You'll be telling me the way, I know.
And it's from the old . . .

4 Give me courage when the world is rough,
keep me loving, though the world is tough.
Leap and sing in all I do,
keep me travelling along with You.
And it's from the old . . .

5 You are older than the world can be.
You are younger than the life in me.
Ever old and ever new,
keep me travelling along with you.
And it's from the old . . .

189

Lisa Mazak
© 1974, 1975 Celebration / Kingsway's Thankyou Music

One, two, three, Jesus loves me.
One, two, Jesus loves you.

1 Three, four, He loves you more
than you've ever been loved before.
One, two, three . . .

2 Five, six, seven, we're going to heaven.
Eight, nine, it's truly divine.
One, two, three . . .

3 Nine, ten, it's time to end,
but instead we'll sing it again
LAST TIME
(there's no time to sing it again).

190

Anon
Copyright control

Only a boy called David,
only a rippling brook;
only a boy called David,
five little stones he took.
Then one little stone went in the sling,
and the sling went round and round,
one little stone went in the sling,
and the sling went round and round.
Round and round and round and round
and round and round and round;
one little stone went up, up, up,
and the giant came tumbling down!

191

© Roland Meredith

1 **Our eyes have seen the glory**
of our Saviour, Christ the Lord;
He is seated at His Father's side
in love and full accord;
from there upon the sons of men
His Spirit is outpoured,
all hail, ascended King!
Glory, glory, hallelujah,
glory, glory, hallelujah,
glory, glory, hallelujah,
all hail, ascended King!

2 He came to earth at Christmas
and was made a man like us;
He taught, He healed, He suffered –
and they nailed Him to the cross;
He rose again on Easter Day –
our Lord victorious,
all hail, ascended King!
Glory, glory . . .

3 The good news of His kingdom
must be preached to every shore,
the news of peace and pardon,
and the end of strife and war;
the secret of His kingdom
is to serve Him evermore,
all hail, ascended King!
Glory, glory . . .

4 His kingdom is a family
of men of every race,
they live their lives in harmony,
enabled by His grace;
they follow His example
till they see Him face to face,
all hail, ascended King!
Glory, glory . . .

192

© 1979 Stainer & Bell / The Methodist Church
Division of Education and Youth

1 **Our Father who is in heaven,**
hallowed be Your name,
Your kingdom come, Your will be done,
hallowed be Your name.

2 On earth as it is in heaven,
hallowed be Your name,
give us this day our daily bread,
hallowed be Your name.

3 Forgive us all our trespasses,
hallowed be Your name,
as we forgive those who trespass against us,
hallowed be Your name.

4 And lead us not into temptation,
hallowed be Your name,
but deliver us from all that is evil,
hallowed be Your name.

5 For Yours is the kingdom,
the power and the glory,
hallowed be Your name,
for ever and for ever and ever,
hallowed be Your name.

6 Amen, amen, it shall be so,
  hallowed be Your name,
  amen, amen, it shall be so,
  hallowed be Your name.

193 Eric A Thorn
© Christian Music Ministries

1 **Our harvest day is over
    for yet another year.**
  The gifts we've brought to Jesus
  are now before us here.
  Before we go, again we raise
    our thanks to God above
  for all that He provides us with
    from His great hand of love.

2 We thank God for providing
    fresh air for us to breathe.
  Thirst-quenching water, also,
    to us He does bequeath.
  Fresh fruit and daily bread as well
    are gifts from God above,
  tinned foods, and eggs, and poultry
    come from our great God of love.

3 Our clothes and health come also
    from God's all-gracious hand;
  our happiness is something
    which He again has planned.
  But something more important still
    comes to us through God's love –
  eternal life, through His dear Son;
    all praise to God above.
  All praise to God above!

194 Spiritual

O sinner man, where will you run to,
O sinner man, where will you run to,
O sinner man, where will you run to,
all on that day?

Run to the rocks, rocks, won't you hide me,
run to the rocks, rocks, won't you hide me,
run to the rocks, rocks, won't you hide me,
all on that day?
O sinner man . . .

Run to the sea, sea is a-boiling,
run to the sea, sea is a-boiling,
run to the sea, sea is a-boiling,
all on that day.
O sinner man . . .

3 Run to the Lord, Lord, won't you hide me,
  run to the Lord, Lord, won't you hide me,
  run to the Lord, Lord, won't you hide me,
  all on that day?
  O sinner man . . .

4 O sinner man, should bin a-praying,
  O sinner man, should bin a-praying,
  O sinner man, should bin a-praying,
  all on that day.
  O sinner man . . .

195 Traditional

1 **O when the saints go marching in,**
  O when the saints go marching in,
  O Lord, I want to be among the number
  when the saints go marching in!

2 O when they crown Him Lord of all,
  O when they crown Him Lord of all,
  O Lord, I want to be among the number
  when they crown Him Lord of all.

3 O when all knees bow at His name,
  O when all knees bow at His name,
  O Lord, I want to be among the number
  when all knees bow at His name.

4 O when they sing the Saviour's praise,
  O when they sing the Saviour's praise,
  O Lord, I want to be among the number
  when they sing the Saviour's praise.

5 O when the saints go marching in,
  O when the saints go marching in,
  O Lord, I want to be among the number
  when the saints go marching in!

196 Graham Kendrick
© 1979 Kingsway's Thankyou Music

1 **Peace I give to you,
    I give to you My peace;**
  peace I give to you, I give to you My peace.
    Let it flow to one another,
    let it flow, let it flow;
    let it flow to one another,
    let it flow, let it flow.

2 Love I give to you, I give to you My love;
  love I give to you, I give to you My love.
    Let it flow . . .

3 Hope I give to you, I give to you My hope;
  hope I give to you, I give to you My hope.
  Let it flow . . .

4 Joy I give to you, I give to you My joy;
  joy I give to you, I give to you My joy.
  Let it flow . . .

2 'Silver and gold have I none,
  but such as I have I give you.
  In the name of Jesus Christ of Nazareth,
  rise up and walk!'

3 He went walking and leaping
      and praising God,
  walking and leaping and praising God.
  'In the name of Jesus Christ of Nazareth,
  rise up and walk!'

197 Anon
Copyright control

1 **Peter and James and John in a sailboat,**
  Peter and James and John in a sailboat,
  Peter and James and John in a sailboat,
  out on the beautiful sea.

2 They fished all night but they
      caught nothing,
  they fished all night but they caught nothing,
  they fished all night but they caught nothing,
  out on the beautiful sea.

3 Along came Jesus walking on the water,
  along came Jesus walking on the water,
  along came Jesus walking on the water,
  out on the beautiful sea.

4 He said, 'Throw your nets over
      on the other side!'
  He said, 'Throw your nets over
      on the other side!'
  He said, 'Throw your nets over
      on the other side!'
  out on the beautiful sea.

5 The nets were filled with great big fishes,
  the nets were filled with great big fishes,
  the nets were filled with great big fishes,
  out on the beautiful sea.

6 The lesson of this story is,
      'listen to the Lord',
  the lesson of this story is, 'listen to the Lord',
  the lesson of this story is, 'listen to the Lord',
  wherever you may be.

198 Anon
Copyright control

1 **Peter and John went to pray,**
  they met a lame man on the way;
  he asked for alms and held out his palms,
  and this is what Peter did say:

199 Thomas Ken (1637–1711)

Praise God from whom all blessings flow;
praise Him all creatures here below,
praise Him above, you heavenly hosts;
praise Father, Son, and Holy Ghost.

200 John Kennett
© 1981 Kingsway's Thankyou Music

**Praise Him on the trumpet,
  the psaltery and harp;**
praise Him on the timbrel and the dance;
praise Him with stringed instruments too;

praise Him on the loud cymbals,
praise Him on the loud cymbals;
let everything that has breath
  praise the Lord!

Hallelujah, praise the Lord;
hallelujah, praise the Lord:
let everything that has breath
  praise the Lord!

Hallelujah, praise the Lord;
hallelujah, praise the Lord:
let everything that has breath
  praise the Lord!

201 Anon, c1890
Copyright control

1 **Praise Him, praise Him,
  all you little children,**
  God is love, God is love.
  Praise Him, praise Him, all you little children
  God is love, God is love.

2 Love Him, love Him, all you little children,
  God is love, God is love.
  Love Him, love Him, all you little children,
  God is love, God is love.

3 Thank Him, thank Him, all you little children,
God is love, God is love.
Thank Him, thank Him, all you little children,
God is love, God is love.

crown Him, crown Him!
Prophet, and Priest, and King!
Christ is coming, over the world victorious,
power and glory unto the Lord belong.
Praise Him . . .

202
Anon
Copyright control

6/98

1 **Praise Him, praise Him,**
praise Him in the morning,
praise Him in the noontime,
praise Him, praise Him,
praise Him as the sun goes down.

2 Thank Him . . .

3 Love Him . . .

4 Serve Him . . .

203
Frances van Alstyne (1820–1915)
(Fanny J Crosby)
altered © 1986 Horrobin / Leavers

Praise Him, praise Him!
Jesus, our blessèd Redeemer!
Sing, O earth – His wonderful love proclaim!
Hail Him, hail Him!
highest archangels in glory;
strength and honour give to his holy name!
Like a shepherd,
Jesus will guard His children,
in His arms He carries them all day long.
Praise Him, praise Him!
tell of His excellent greatness;
praise Him, praise Him
ever in joyful song!

Praise Him, praise Him!
Jesus, our blessèd Redeemer!
For our sins He suffered, and bled, and died;
He – our rock, our hope of eternal salvation,
hail Him, hail Him! Jesus the crucified!
Sound His praises –
Jesus who bore our sorrows,
love unbounded, wonderful,
deep and strong.
Praise Him . . .

Praise Him, praise Him!
Jesus, our blessèd Redeemer!
All in heaven, let their hosannas ring!
Jesus, Saviour, reigning for ever and ever:

204
Henry Francis Lyte (1793–1847)

1 **Praise, my soul, the King of heaven;**
to His feet your worship bring;
ransomed, healed, restored, forgiven,
we do now His praises sing.
Praise Him! Praise Him!
Praise Him! Praise Him!
Praise the everlasting King.

2 Praise Him for His grace and favour
to our fathers, in distress;
praise Him, still the same for ever;
merciful, He waits to bless.
Praise Him! Praise Him!
Praise Him! Praise Him!
Glorious in His faithfulness.

3 Father-like He loves and spares us;
well our weaknesses He knows;
in His hands He gently bears us,
rescues us from all our foes.
Praise Him! Praise Him!
Praise Him! Praise Him!
Widely as His mercy flows.

4 Angels, help us to adore Him;
you behold Him face to face;
sun and moon, bow down before Him;
dwellers all in time and space.
Praise Him! Praise Him!
Praise Him! Praise Him!
Praise with us the God of grace.

205
Estelle White
© McCrimmon Publishing Co Ltd

Praise to the Lord our God,
let us sing together,
lifting our hearts and our voices to sing
with joy and gladness.
Come along, along, along
and sing with praise.

206

This song has been withdrawn
for copyright-related reasons

207
Percy Dearmer (1867–1936)
From *Enlarged Songs of Praise*
by permission of Oxford University Press

1 **Remember all the people**
who live in far off lands,
in strange and lovely cities,
or roam the desert sands,
or farm the mountain pastures,
or till the endless plains
where children wade through rice fields
and watch the camel trains.

2 Some work in sultry forests
where apes swing to and fro,
some fish in mighty rivers,
some hunt across the snow.
Remember all God's children
who yet have never heard
the truth that comes from Jesus,
the glory of His word.

3 God bless the men and women
who serve Him oversea:
God raise up more to help them
to set the nations free,
till all the distant people
in every foreign place
shall understand His kingdom
and come into His grace.

208
From Philippians 4
Copyright control

Rejoice in the Lord always,
and again I say rejoice!
Rejoice in the Lord always,
and again I say rejoice!
Rejoice, rejoice, and again I say rejoice!
Rejoice, rejoice, and again I say rejoice!

209
Henry Hart Milman (1791–1868)
© in this version Jubilate Hymns

1 **Ride on, ride on in majesty**
as all the crowds, 'Hosanna!' cry:
through waving branches slowly ride,
O Saviour, to be crucified.

2 Ride on, ride on in majesty,
in lowly pomp ride on to die:
O Christ, your triumph now begin
with captured death and conquered sin!

3 Ride on, ride on in majesty –
the angel armies of the sky
look down with sad and wondering eyes
to see the approaching sacrifice.

4 Ride on, ride on in majesty,
the last and fiercest foe defy:
the Father on His sapphire throne
awaits His own anointed Son.

5 Ride on, ride on in majesty,
in lowly pomp ride on to die:
bow Your meek head to mortal pain,
then take, O God, Your power and reign!

210 Traditional

Rise and shine and give God
His glory, glory,
rise and shine and give God
His glory, glory,
rise and shine and give God
His glory, glory,
children of the Lord.

1 The Lord said to Noah,
'There's gonna be a floody, floody.'
Lord said to Noah,
'There's gonna be a floody, floody.
Get those children out of the muddy, muddy
children of the Lord.'
Rise and shine . . .

2 The Lord told Noah to build Him
an arky, arky,
the Lord told Noah to build Him
an arky, arky,
build it out of gopher barky, barky,
children of the Lord.
Rise and shine . . .

3 The animals, the animals,
they came on by twosies, twosies,
the animals, the animals,
they came on by twosies, twosies,
elephants and kangaroosies, 'roosies,
children of the Lord.
Rise and shine . . .

4 It rained and poured for
forty daysies, daysies,
it rained and poured for
forty daysies, daysies,
almost drove those animals crazies, crazies
children of the Lord.
Rise and shine . . .

5 The sun came out and dried up the
       landy, landy,
   the sun came out and dried up the
       landy, landy.
   Everything was fine and dandy, dandy,
   children of the Lord.
       Rise and shine . . .

211 Sydney Carter
         © 1964 Stainer & Bell Ltd

1 **Said Judas to Mary, 'Now what will you do**
   with your ointment so rich and so rare?'
   'I'll pour it all over the feet of the Lord
   and I'll wipe it away with my hair,' she said,
   'I'll wipe it away with my hair.'

2 'O Mary, O Mary, O think of the poor –
   this ointment it could have been sold,
   and think of the blankets
       and think of the bread
   you could buy with the silver and gold,'
       he said,
   'you could buy with the silver and gold.'

3 'Tomorrow, tomorrow I'll think of the poor,
   tomorrow,' she said, 'not today;
   for dearer than all of the poor of the world
   is my love who is going away,' she said,
   'is my love who is going away.'

4 Said Jesus to Mary, 'Your love is so deep,
   today you may do as you will;
   tomorrow, you say, I am going away,
   but My body I leave with you still,' He said,
   'My body I leave with you still.'

5 'The poor of the world are My body,'
       He said,
   'to the end of the world they shall be;
   the bread and the blankets
       you give to the poor
   you'll find you have given to Me,' He said,
   'you'll find you have given to Me.'

6 'My body will hang on the cross of the world
   tomorrow,' He said, 'and today,
   and Martha and Mary will find Me again
   and wash all My sorrow away,' He said,
   'and wash all my sorrow away.'

212

This song has been withdrawn
for copyright-related reasons

213 Edward Caswall (1814–78)
         altered © 1986 Horrobin / Leavers

1 **See, amid the winter snow,**
   born for us on earth below;
   see, the Son of God appears,
   promised from eternal years.
       Hail, O ever-blessèd morn!
       Hail, redemption's happy dawn!
       Sing through all Jerusalem,
       Christ is born in Bethlehem!

2 Low within a manger lies
   He who built the starry skies,
   He who, throned in heaven's height
   reigns in power and glorious light.
       Hail, O ever-blessèd morn . . .

3 Say, you humble shepherds, say,
   what's your joyful news today?
   Tell us why you left your sheep
   on the lonely mountain steep:
       Hail, O ever-blessèd morn . . .

4 'As we watched at dead of night,
   all around us shone a light:
   angels singing, "Peace on earth!"
   told us of a Saviour's birth.'
       Hail, O ever-blessèd morn . . .

5 Sacred baby, King most dear,
   what a tender love was here!
   Down He came from glory high
   in a manger there to lie.
       Hail, O ever-blessèd morn . . .

6 Holy Saviour, born on earth,
   teach us by Your lowly birth;
   grant that we may ever be
   taught by such humility.
       Hail, O ever-blessèd morn . . .

214 Michael Perry (1942–96)
         © Executors of the late Michael Perry / Jubilate Hymns

1 **See Him lying on a bed of straw:**
   a draughty stable with an open door;
   Mary cradling the babe she bore –
   the Prince of glory is His name.
       O now carry me to Bethlehem
       to see the Lord appear to men –
       just as poor as was the stable then,
       the Prince of glory when He came.

2 Star of silver, sweep across the skies,
show where Jesus in the manger lies;
shepherds, swiftly from your stupor rise
to see the Saviour of the world!
O now carry . . .

3 Angels, sing the song that you began,
bring God's glory to the heart of man;
sing that Bethl'em's little baby can
be salvation to the soul.
O now carry . . .

4 Mine are riches, from Your poverty,
from Your innocence, eternity;
mine forgiveness by Your death for me,
child of sorrow for my joy.
O now carry . . .

215 Karen Lafferty
© 1972 Maranatha! Music /
CopyCare Ltd

1 **Seek ye first the kingdom of God,**
and His righteousness,
and all these things shall be added unto you.
Allelu, alleluia.
Seek ye first . . .

2 Man shall not live by bread alone,
but by every word
that proceeds from the mouth of God.
Allelu, alleluia.
Man shall not . . .

3 Ask and it shall be given unto you,
seek and ye shall find;
knock and the door shall be opened
up to you.
Allelu, alleluia.
Ask and it shall . . .

216 © 1986 Greg Leavers

Saviour of the world,
thank You for dying on the cross.
All praise to You, our risen Lord,
hallelujah! Jesus.

1 In the garden of Gethsemane
Jesus knelt and prayed;
for He knew the time was near
when He would be betrayed.
God gave Him the strength to cope with all
that people did to hurt Him;
soldiers laughed and forced a crown of
thorns upon His head.
Saviour of the world . . .

2 On a cross outside the city
they nailed Jesus high;
innocent, but still He suffered
as they watched Him die.
Nothing that the soldiers did could make
Him lose control, for Jesus
knew the time to die, then,
'It is finished!' was His cry.
Saviour of the world . . .

3 Three days later by God's power
He rose up from the dead,
for the tomb could not hold Jesus,
it was as He'd said;
victor over sin and death,
He conquered Satan's power; so let us
celebrate that Jesus is alive for evermore.
Saviour of the world . . .

217 Michael Lehr
© Stainer & Bell Ltd

Shalōm, my friend, shalōm, my friend,
shalōm, shalōm.
Till we meet again, till we meet again,
shalōm, shalōm.

218 Charles Silvester Horne (1865–1914)

1 **Sing we the King who is coming to reign,**
glory to Jesus, the Lamb that was slain;
life and salvation His coming shall bring,
joy to the nations when Jesus is King.
Come let us sing: praise to our King.
Jesus our King, Jesus our King:
this is our song, who to Jesus belong:
glory to Jesus, to Jesus our King.

2 All men who dwell in His marvellous light,
races long severed His love shall unite;
justice and truth
from His sceptre shall spring,
wrong shall be ended when Jesus is King.
Come let us sing . . .

3 All shall be well in His kingdom of peace,
   freedom and wisdom
       and love shall not cease;
   foe shall be friend when His triumph we sing,
   sword shall be sickle when Jesus is King.
       Come let us sing . . .

4 Souls shall be saved from the burden of sin;
   doubt shall not darken his witness within;
   hell has no terrors, and death has no sting;
   love is victorious, when Jesus is King.
       Come let us sing . . .

5 Kingdom of Christ, for your coming we pray;
   hasten, O Father, the dawn of the day
   when this new song Your creation shall sing,
   Satan is conquered and Jesus is King.
       Come let us sing . . .

219   Joseph Mohr (1792–1848)
          tr. Stopford Augustus Brooke (1832–1916)

1 **Silent night, holy night!**
   Sleeps the world; hid from sight,
   Mary and Joseph in stable bare
   watched o'er the child belovèd and fair
       sleeping in heavenly rest,
       sleeping in heavenly rest.

2 Silent night, holy night!
   Shepherds first saw the light,
   heard resounding clear and long,
   far and near, the angel-song:
       'Christ the Redeemer is here,
       Christ the Redeemer is here.'

3 Silent night, holy night!
   Son of God, O how bright
   love is smiling from Your face!
   Strikes for us now the hour of grace,
       Saviour, since You are born,
       Saviour, since You are born.

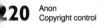

220   Anon
          Copyright control

Someone's brought a loaf of bread,
someone's brought a loaf of bread,
someone's brought a loaf of bread
to put on the harvest table.

Someone's brought a jar of jam,
someone's brought a jar of jam,
someone's brought a jar of jam
to put on the harvest table.

Other verses may be added

Last verse:

   Thank You, Lord, for all Your gifts,
   thank You, Lord, for all Your gifts,
   thank You, Lord, for all Your gifts
   to put on the harvest table.

221   Andrae Crouch
          © 1978 Bud John Songs / Crouch Music /
          Alliance Media Ltd / CopyCare Ltd

1 **Soon, and very soon,**
   we are going to see the King;
   soon, and very soon,
   we are going to see the King;
   soon, and very soon,
   we are going to see the King;
       alleluia, alleluia,
       we're going to see the King!

2 No more crying there . . .
       alleluia . . .

3 No more dying there . . .
       alleluia . . .
       Alleluia, alleluia, alleluia, alleluia.

4 Soon and very soon . . .
       alleluia . . .
       Alleluia, alleluia, alleluia, alleluia.

222   Daniel Iverson
          © 1963 Birdwing Music / Alliance Media Ltd /
          CopyCare Ltd

Spirit of the living God,
   fall afresh on me;
Spirit of the living God,
   fall afresh on me;
break me, melt me,
   mould me, fill me;
Spirit of the living God,
   fall afresh on me.

223   Alfred B Smith and John W Peterson
          © 1954 Singspiration Music / Fine Balance Music /
          CopyCare Ltd

Surely goodness and mercy
   shall follow me
all the days, all the days of my life;
surely goodness and mercy shall follow me
all the days, all the days of my life.
And I shall dwell in the house
   of the Lord forever,
and I shall feast at the table spread for me.
Surely goodness and mercy shall follow me
all the days, all the days of my life.

224

© 1986 Andy Silver

Stand up and bless the Lord your God,
stand up and bless the Lord;
His name is exalted above all names;
stand up and bless the Lord.

For our God is good to us,
always ready to forgive;
He is gracious and merciful,
slow to anger and very kind.

So, stand up and bless the Lord your God,
stand up and bless the Lord;
stand up and bless the Lord your God,
stand up.

225

Roger Dyer
© 1970 High-Fye Music Ltd

*Stand up, clap hands, shout,
'Thank You, Lord,
thank You for the world I'm in.'
Stand up, clap hands, shout,
'Thank You, Lord,
for happiness and peace within.'*

1 I look around and the sun's in the sky,
I look around and then I think, 'Oh, my!'
The world is such a wonderful place,
and all because of the good Lord's grace.
Stand up, clap hands . . .

2 I look around and the creatures I see,
I look around and it amazes me
that every fox and bird and hare
must fit in a special place somewhere.
Stand up, clap hands . . .

3 I look around at all the joy I've had,
I look around and then it makes me glad
that I can offer thanks and praise
to Him who guides me through my days.
Stand up, clap hands . . .

226

George Duffield (1818–88)
© in this version Jubilate Hymns

1 **Stand up! stand up for Jesus!**
you soldiers of the cross,
lift high His royal banner;
it must not suffer loss.
From victory unto victory
His army He shall lead,
till evil is defeated
and Christ is Lord indeed.

2 Stand up! stand up for Jesus!
the trumpet-call obey;
then join the mighty conflict
in this His glorious day.
Be strong in faith and serve Him
against unnumbered foes;
let courage rise with danger,
and strength to strength oppose.

3 Stand up! stand up for Jesus!
stand in His power alone;
for human might will fail you,
you dare not trust your own.
Put on the gospel armour,
keep watch with constant prayer;
where duty calls, or danger,
be never failing there.

4 Stand up! stand up for Jesus!
the fight will not be long;
this day the noise of battle,
the next the victor's song.
To everyone who conquers
a crown of life shall be;
we with the King of glory
shall reign eternally.

227

Arabella Catherine Hankey (1834–1911) altd.

1 **Tell me the old, old story**
of unseen things above,
of Jesus and His glory,
of Jesus and His love.
Tell me the story simply,
as to a little child,
for I am weak and weary,
and helpless and defiled.
*Tell me the old, old story,
tell me the old, old story,
tell me the old, old story
of Jesus and His love.*

2 Tell me the story slowly,
that I may take it in –
that wonderful redemption,
God's remedy for sin.
Tell me the story often,
for I forget so soon:
the early dew of morning
has passed away at noon.
Tell me the old . . .

3 Tell me the story softly,
with earnest tones and grave;
Remember! I'm the sinner
whom Jesus came to save.
Tell me the story always,
if you would really be,
in any time of trouble,
a comforter to me.
Tell me the old . . .

4 Tell me the same old story,
when you have cause to fear
that this world's empty glory
is costing me too dear.
Yes, and when that world's glory
is dawning on my soul,
tell me the old, old story;
'Christ Jesus makes you whole.'
Tell me the old . . .

4 Into the city I'd follow
the children's band,
waving a branch of the palm-tree
high in my hand;
worshipping Jesus,
yes, I would sing
loudest hosannas,
for He is King!

5 Show me that scene in the garden,
of bitter pain;
and of the cross where my Saviour
for me was slain;
and, through the sadness,
help me to see
how Jesus suffered
for love of me.

6 Gladly I'd hear of His rising
out of the grave,
living and strong and triumphant,
mighty to save:
and how He sends us
all men to bring
stories of Jesus,
Jesus, their King.

228 William Henry Parker (1845–1929)
v.6 Hugh Martin (1890–1964)
adapted Horrobin / Leavers by permission of
the National Christian Education Council

Tell me the stories of Jesus
I love to hear;
things I would ask Him to tell me
if He were here;
scenes by the wayside,
tales of the sea,
stories of Jesus,
tell them to me.

First let me hear how the children
stood round His knee;
that I may know of His blessing
resting on me;
words full of kindness,
deeds full of grace,
signs of the love found
in Jesus' face.

Tell me, in words full of wonder,
how rolled the sea,
tossing the boat in a tempest
on Galilee.
Jesus then doing
His Father's will,
ended the storm saying,
'Peace, peace, be still.'

229 © Timothy Dudley-Smith

1 **Tell out, my soul,
the greatness of the Lord;**
unnumbered blessings give my spirit voice;
tender to me the promise of His word;
in God my Saviour shall my heart rejoice.

2 Tell out, my soul, the greatness of His name!
Make known His might,
the deeds His arm has done;
His mercy sure, from age to age the same;
His holy name – the Lord, the Mighty One.

3 Tell out, my soul, the greatness of His might!
powers and dominions lay their glory by;
proud hearts and stubborn wills
are put to flight,
the hungry fed, the humble lifted high.

4 Tell out, my soul, the glories of His word!
firm is His promise, and His mercy sure:
tell out, my soul, the greatness of the Lord
to children's children and for evermore!

230

M G Schneider
tr. and adpt. S Lonsdale and Michael Baughen
© Bosworth & Co Ltd

1 **Thank You for every new good morning,**
thank You for every fresh new day,
thank You that I may cast my burdens
wholly on to You.

2 Thank You for every friend I have, Lord,
thank You for everyone I know,
thank You when I can feel forgiveness
to my greatest foe.

3 Thank You for leisure and employment,
thank You for every heartfelt joy,
thank You for all that makes me happy
and for melody.

4 Thank You for every shade and sorrow,
thank You for comfort in Your word,
thank You that I am guided by You
everywhere I go.

5 Thank You for grace to know Your gospel,
thank You for all Your Spirit's power,
thank You for Your unfailing love
which reaches far and near.

6 Thank You for free and full salvation,
thank You for grace to hold it fast.
Thank You, O Lord, I want to thank You
that I'm free to thank!
Thank You, O Lord, I want to thank You
that I'm free to thank!

231

Anon
Copyright control

1 **Thank You, thank You, Jesus,**
thank You, thank You, Jesus,
thank You, thank You, Jesus, in my heart.
Thank You, thank You, Jesus,
O thank You, thank You, Jesus,
thank You, thank You, Jesus, in my heart.

2 You can't make me doubt Him,
you can't make me doubt Him,
you can't make me doubt Him in my heart.
You can't make me doubt Him,
O you can't make me doubt Him,
thank You, thank You, Jesus, in my heart.

3 I can't live without Him,
I can't live without Him,
I can't live without Him in my heart.
I can't live without Him,
O I can't live without Him,
thank You, thank You, Jesus, in my heart.

4 Glory, hallelujah,
glory, hallelujah,
glory, hallelujah in my heart!
Glory, hallelujah,
O glory, hallelujah,
thank You, thank You, Jesus, in my heart.

232

Diane Davis Andrew
© 1971, 1975 Celebration / Kingsway's Thankyou Music

1 **Thank You, Lord, for this fine day,**
thank You, Lord, for this fine day,
thank You, Lord, for this fine day,
right where we are.
Alleluia, praise the Lord!
Alleluia, praise the Lord!
Alleluia, praise the Lord,
right where we are.

2 Thank You, Lord, for loving us,
thank You, Lord, for loving us,
thank You, Lord, for loving us,
right where we are.
Alleluia . . .

3 Thank You, Lord, for giving us peace,
thank You, Lord, for giving us peace,
thank You, Lord, for giving us peace,
right where we are.
Alleluia . . .

4 Thank You, Lord, for setting us free,
thank You, Lord, for setting us free,
thank You, Lord, for setting us free,
right where we are.
Alleluia . . .

233

Anon
Copyright control

Thank You, God, for sending Jesus;
thank You, Jesus, that You came;
Holy Spirit, won't You tell us
more about His wondrous name?

234

P Bilhorn (1865–1936)
Copyright control

1 **The best book to read is the Bible,**
the best book to read is the Bible;
if you read it every day
it will help you on your way,
Oh, the best book to read is the Bible.

2   The best friend to have is Jesus,
    the best friend to have is Jesus;
    He will hear me when I call,
    He will keep me lest I fall,
    Oh, the best friend to have is Jesus.

3   The best thing to do is to trust Him,
    the best thing to do is to trust Him;
    and if you on Him depend,
    He will keep you to the end;
    Oh, the best thing to do is to trust Him.

235 Alison Huntley
© 1978 Kingsway's Thankyou Music

1   **Thank You, Jesus, thank You, Jesus,**
    thank You, Lord, for loving me.
    Thank You, Jesus . . .

2   You went to Calvary, there You died for me,
    thank You, Lord, for loving me.
    You went to Calvary . . .

3   You rose up from the grave,
        to me new life You gave,
    thank You, Lord, for loving me.
    You rose up from the grave . . .

4   You're coming back again,
        and we with You shall reign,
    thank You, Lord, for loving me.
    You're coming back again . . .

236 John Ellerton (1826–93)
© in this version Jubilate Hymns

1   **The day You gave us, Lord, is ended,**
    the sun is sinking in the west;
    to You our morning hymns ascended,
    Your praise shall sanctify our rest.

2   We thank You that Your Church, unsleeping
    while earth rolls onward into light,
    through all the world her watch is keeping,
    and rests not now by day or night.

3   As to each continent and island
    the dawn proclaims another day,
    the voice of prayer is never silent,
    nor dies the sound of praise away.

4   The sun, that bids us rest, is waking
    Your church beneath the western sky;
    fresh voices hour by hour are making
    Your mighty deeds resound on high.

5   So be it, Lord, Your throne shall never,
    like earth's proud empires, pass away;
    Your kingdom stands, and grows for ever,
    until there dawns that glorious day.

237 © Michael Baughen / Jubilate Hymns

1   **The fields are white unto harvest time,**
    look up and see,
    the fields are white unto harvest time,
    look up and see!
    Pray to the Lord of the harvest,
    Christ says, 'Pray!'
    Pray to the Lord for the workers
    which we need in this day.

2   The harvest truly is fit to reap
    but workers few,
    the harvest truly is fit to reap
    but workers few.
    Pray to the Lord . . .

3   Who else will go into all the world
    to preach the word?
    Who else will go into all the world
    to preach the word?
    Pray to the Lord . . .

4   The Lord's return may be very soon,
    the time is short,
    the Lord's return may be very soon,
    the time is short!
    Pray to the Lord . . .

238 Anon (17th century)
© in this version Jubilate Hymns

1   **The first nowell the angel did say,**
    was to Bethlehem's shepherds
        in fields as they lay;
    in fields where they lay keeping their sheep
    on a cold winter's night that was so deep:
    Nowell, nowell, nowell, nowell,
    born is the King of Israel!

2   Then wise men from a country far
    looked up and saw a guiding star;
    they travelled on by night and day
    to reach the place where Jesus lay:
    Nowell, nowell . . .

3 At Bethlehem they entered in,
on bended knee they worshipped Him;
they offered there in His presence
their gold and myrrh and frankincense:
Nowell, nowell . . .

4 Then let us all with one accord
sing praises to our heavenly Lord;
for Christ has our salvation wrought
and with His blood mankind has bought:
Nowell, nowell . . .

2 If you want joy you must sing for it,
if you want joy you must sing for it,
if you want joy you must sing for it,
the joy of the Lord is my strength.

3 If you want joy you must shout for it,
if you want joy you must shout for it,
if you want joy you must shout for it,
the joy of the Lord is my strength.

4 If you want joy you must jump for it,
if you want joy you must jump for it,
if you want joy you must jump for it,
the joy of the Lord is my strength.

 239 Mark Pendergrass
© 1977 Birdwing Music / BMG Songs Inc /
Garden Valley Music / Alliance Media Ltd /
CopyCare Ltd

1 **The greatest thing in all my life**
is knowing You;
the greatest thing in all my life
is knowing You;
I want to know You more;
I want to know You more.
The greatest thing in all my life
is knowing You.

2 The greatest thing in all my life
is loving You;
the greatest thing in all my life
is loving You;
I want to love You more;
I want to love You more.
The greatest thing in all my life
is loving You.

3 The greatest thing in all my life
is serving You;
the greatest thing in all my life
is serving You;
I want to serve You more;
I want to serve You more.
The greatest thing in all my life
is serving You.

 241 Henry Williams Baker (1821–77)
© in this version Jubilate Hymns

1 **The King of love my shepherd is,**
whose goodness fails me never;
I nothing lack if I am His
and He is mine for ever.

2 Where streams of living water flow,
a ransomed soul, He leads me;
and where the fertile pastures grow
with food from heaven feeds me.

3 Perverse and foolish I have strayed;
but in His love He sought me,
and on His shoulder gently laid,
and home, rejoicing, brought me.

4 In death's dark vale I fear no ill
with You, dear Lord, beside me;
Your rod and staff my comfort still,
Your cross before to guide me.

5 You spread a banquet in my sight
of love beyond all knowing,
and O the gladness and delight
from Your pure chalice flowing!

6 And so through all the length of days
Your goodness fails me never;
Good Shepherd, may I sing Your praise
within Your house for ever!

240 Alliene Vale
© 1978 His Eye Music / Multisongs /
Joy of the Lord Music / Alliance Media Ltd /
CopyCare Ltd

1 **The joy of the Lord is my strength,**
the joy of the Lord is my strength,
the joy of the Lord is my strength,
the joy of the Lord is my strength.

242 Cecil J Allen
© F R Allen

The Lord has need of me,
His soldier I will be;
He gave Himself my life to win,
and so I mean to follow Him,
and serve Him faithfully.

So although the fight be fierce and long,
I'll carry on: He makes me strong;
and then one day His face I'll see,
and O the joy when He says to me,
'Well done, my brave crusader!'

243 Francis Rous (1579–1659)
revised for *Scottish Psalter*, 1650
altered © 1986 Horrobin / Leavers

1 **The Lord's my shepherd, I'll not want;**
He makes me down to lie
in pastures green; He's leading me
the quiet waters by.

2 My soul He does restore again,
and me to walk does make
within the paths of righteousness,
e'en for His own name's sake.

3 Yes, though I walk through death's dark vale,
yet will I fear no ill;
for You are with me, and Your rod
and staff me comfort still.

4 My table You have furnishèd
in presence of my foes;
my head You now with oil anoint,
and my cup overflows.

5 Goodness and mercy all my life
shall surely follow me;
and in God's house for evermore
my dwelling-place shall be.

244 From Psalm 23
Copyright control

The Lord is my shepherd,
I'll trust in Him always.
He leads me by still waters,
I'll trust in Him always.
Always, always, I'll trust in Him always.
Always, always, I'll trust in Him always.

245 Cecil Frances Alexander (1818–95)

There is a green hill far away
outside a city wall,
where the dear Lord was crucified,
who died to save us all.

2 We may not know, we cannot tell
what pains He had to bear;
but we believe it was for us
He hung and suffered there.

3 He died that we might be forgiven,
He died to make us good,
that we might go at last to heaven,
saved by His precious blood.

4 There was no other good enough
to pay the price of sin;
He only could unlock the gate
of heaven, and let us in.

5 O dearly, dearly has He loved,
and we must love Him too,
and trust in His redeeming blood,
and try His works to do.

246 John Gowans
© 1970 Salvationist Publishing and Supplies Ltd /
CopyCare Ltd

1 **There are hundreds of sparrows,**
    thousands, millions,
    they're two a penny,
        far too many there must be;
    there are hundreds and thousands,
        millions of sparrows,
    but God knows every one
        and God knows me.

2 There are hundreds of flowers,
        thousands, millions,
    and flowers fair the meadows
        wear for all to see;
    there are hundreds and thousands,
        millions of flowers,
    but God knows every one
        and God knows me.

3 There are hundreds of planets,
        thousands, millions,
    way out in space each has a place
        by God's decree;
    there are hundreds and thousands,
        millions of planets,
    but God knows every one
        and God knows me.

4 There are hundreds of children,
    thousands, millions,
and yet their names are written
    on God's memory;
there are hundreds and thousands,
    millions of children,
but God knows every one
    and God knows me,
but God knows every one
    and God knows me.

250

Edith McNeill
© 1974 Celebration / Kingsway's Thankyou Music

The steadfast love of the Lord
    never ceases,
His mercies never come to an end;
they are new every morning,
    new every morning:
great is Your faithfulness, O Lord,
great is Your faithfulness.

247

Anon
Copyright control

ALL **There's a song of exaltation**
    full of joy and inspiration
    echoed down through all creation,
    sing hallelujah, sing.

PART 1 Sing hallelujah,
PART 2 sing hallelujah,
PART 1 sing hallelujah,
PART 2 sing hallelujah,
PART 1 sing hallelujah,
PART 2 sing hallelujah,
ALL   sing hallelujah, sing.

248

E H Swinstead (d1976)
Copyright control

There's a way back to God
    from the dark paths of sin;
there's a door that is open
    and you may go in:
at Calvary's cross is where you begin,
when you come as a sinner to Jesus.

249

Anon
Copyright control

1 **There's new life in Jesus,**
    lift up your heart,
there's new life in Jesus, lift up your heart.
    Lift up your heart, lift up your heart,
    there's new life in Jesus, lift up your heart.

2 There is healing in His love, lift up your heart,
there is healing in His love, lift up your heart.
    Lift up your heart . . .

3 There is joy in serving Him, lift up your heart,
there is joy in serving Him, lift up your heart.
    Lift up your heart . . .

251

Anon
Copyright control

1 **The virgin Mary had a baby boy,**
the virgin Mary had a baby boy,
the virgin Mary had a baby boy
and they said that His name was Jesus.
    He come from the glory,
    He come from the glorious kingdom,
    He come from the glory,
    He come from the glorious kingdom.
    O yes, believer,
    O yes, believer,
    He come from the glory,
    He come from the glorious kingdom.

2 The angels sang when the baby was born,
the angels sang when the baby was born,
the angels sang when the baby was born,
and proclaimed Him the Saviour Jesus.
    He come from the glory . . .

3 The wise men saw where the baby
    was born,
the wise men saw where the baby was born,
the wise men saw where the baby was born,
and they saw that His name was Jesus.
    He come from the glory . . .

6/98

252

Anon
Copyright control

1 **The wise man built his house**
    upon the rock,
the wise man built his house upon the rock,
the wise man built his house upon the rock
and the rain came tumbling down.
And the rain came down and the
    floods came up,
the rain came down and the floods came up
the rain came down and the floods came up
and the house on the rock stood firm.

2 The foolish man built his house
       upon the sand,
   the foolish man built his house
       upon the sand,
   the foolish man built his house
       upon the sand
   and the rain came tumbling down.
   And the rain came down and the
       floods came up,
   the rain came down and the floods came up,
   the rain came down and the floods came up
   and the house on the sand fell flat.

253 From the *Book of Praise for Children*, 1881
altered

The wise may bring their learning,
the rich may bring their wealth,
and some may bring their greatness,
and some their strength and health.
We too would bring our treasures
to offer to the King;
we have no wealth or learning,
what gifts then shall we bring?

We'll bring the many duties
we have to do each day.
We'll try our best to please Him
at home, at school, at play,
and better are these treasures
to offer to the King
than richest gifts without them,
yet these we all may bring.

We'll bring Him hearts that love Him,
we'll bring Him thankful praise,
and lives for ever striving
to follow in His ways,
and these shall be the treasures
we offer to the King,
and these are gifts that ever
our grateful hearts may bring.

254 Doreen Newport
© 1969 Stainer & Bell Ltd

Think of a world without any flowers,
think of a world without any trees,
think of a sky without any sunshine,
think of the air without any breeze.
We thank You, Lord, for flowers and trees
    and sunshine,
we thank You, Lord, and praise
    Your holy name.

2 Think of a world without any animals,
   think of a field without any herd,
   think of a stream without any fishes,
   think of a dawn without any bird.
   We thank You, Lord, for all Your
       living creatures,
   we thank You, Lord, and praise
       Your holy name.

3 Think of a world without any people,
   think of a street with no-one living there,
   think of a town without any houses,
   no-one to love and nobody to care.
   We thank You, Lord, for families
       and friendships,
   we thank You, Lord, and praise
       Your holy name.

255 Les Garrett
© 1967 Scripture in Song /
Integrity's Hosanna! Music / Kingsway's Thankyou Music

1 **This is the day,**
   this is the day that the Lord has made,
   that the Lord has made.
   We will rejoice,
   we will rejoice and be glad in it,
   and be glad in it.
   This is the day that the Lord has made,
   we will rejoice and be glad in it.
   This is the day,
   this is the day that the Lord has made.

2 This is the day,
   this is the day when He rose again,
   when He rose again.
   We will rejoice,
   we will rejoice and be glad in it,
   and be glad in it.
   This is the day when He rose again,
   we will rejoice and be glad in it.
   This is the day,
   this is the day when He rose again.

3 This is the day,
   this is the day when the Spirit came,
   when the Spirit came.
   We will rejoice,
   we will rejoice and be glad in it,
   and be glad in it.
   This is the day when the Spirit came,
   we will rejoice and be glad in it.
   This is the day,
   this is the day when the Spirit came.

256 Fred Pratt Green
© 1969 Stainer & Bell Ltd

1 **This joyful Eastertide,**
what need is there for grieving?
Cast all your care aside
and be not unbelieving:
Come, share our Easter joy
that death could not imprison,
nor any power destroy,
our Christ, who is arisen,
arisen, arisen, arisen!

2 No work for Him is vain,
no faith in Him mistaken,
for Easter makes it plain
His kingdom is not shaken:
Come, share our Easter joy . . .

3 Then put your trust in Christ,
in waking or in sleeping.
His grace on earth sufficed;
He'll never quit His keeping:
Come, share our Easter joy . . .

257 © 1964 Richard Bewes / Jubilate Hymns

1 **Though the world has forsaken God,**
treads a different path, lives a different way,
I walk the road that the Saviour trod,
and all may know I live under Jesus' sway.
They are watching you, marking all you do,
hearing the things you say;
let them see the Saviour
as He shines in you,
let His power control you every day.

2 Men will look at the life I lead,
see the side I take and the things I love;
they judge my Lord by my every deed –
Lord, set my affections on things above.
They are watching you . . .

3 When assailed in temptation's hour
by besetting sins, by the fear of man,
then I can know Jesus' mighty power,
and become like Him in His perfect plan.
They are watching you . . .

4 Here on earth people walk in the night;
with no lamp to guide they are dead in sin.
I know the Lord who can give them light,
I live, yet not I, but Christ within.
They are watching you . . .

258 Traditional

This little light of mine,
I'm gonna let it shine,
this little light of mine,
I'm gonna let it shine.
This little light of mine,
I'm gonna let it shine,
let it shine, let it shine, let it shine.

1 The light that shines is the light of love,
lights the darkness from above.
It shines on me and it shines on you,
and shows what the power of love can do.
I'm gonna shine my light both far and near,
I'm gonna shine my light
both bright and clear.
Where there's a dark corner in this land
I'm gonna let my little light shine.
This little light of mine . . .

2 On Monday, He gave me the gift of love,
Tuesday, peace came from above.
On Wednesday He told me
to have more faith,
on Thursday He gave me a little more grace
Friday, He told me just to watch and pray,
Saturday, He told me just what to say.
On Sunday He gave me the power divine
to let my little light shine.
This little light of mine . . .

259 Frances van Alstyne (1820–1915)
(Fanny J Crosby)

1 **To God be the glory!**
great things He has done;
so loved He the world
that He gave us His Son;
who yielded His life an atonement for sin,
and opened the life gate that all may go in.
Praise the Lord, praise the Lord!
let the earth hear His voice;
praise the Lord, praise the Lord!
let the people rejoice:
O come to the Father,
through Jesus the Son
and give Him the glory;
great things He has done!

2 O perfect redemption,
the purchase of blood!
to every believer the promise of God;
the vilest offender who truly believes,
that moment from Jesus a pardon receives
Praise the Lord . . .

Great things He has taught us,
    great things He has done,
and great our rejoicing
    through Jesus the Son;
but purer, and higher, and greater will be
our wonder, our rapture, when Jesus we see.
Praise the Lord . . .

260
Helen H Lemmel (1864–1961)
© 1922, 1950 Singspiration Music /
Fine Balance Music / CopyCare Ltd

Turn your eyes upon Jesus,
look full in His wonderful face;
and the things of earth
    will grow strangely dim
in the light of His glory and grace.

Keep your eyes upon Jesus,
let nobody else take His place;
so that hour by hour you will know
    His power
till at last you have run the great race.

61
© 1945 Hugh Mitchell
Copyright control

Twelve men went to spy in Canaan,
ten were bad, two were good.
What did they see when they spied
    in Canaan?
Ten were bad, two were good.
Some saw giants tough and tall,
some saw grapes in clusters fall,
some saw God was in it all,
ten were bad, two were good.

62
C C Kerr
© Mrs B K M Kerr

Two little eyes to look to God,
two little ears to hear His word,
two little feet to walk in His ways,
two little lips to sing His praise,
two little hands to do His will,
and one little heart to love Him still.

263
German (15th century)
tr. Percy Dearmer (1867–1936)
From the *Oxford Book of Carols*
by permission of Oxford University Press

1   **Unto us a boy is born!**
    King of all creation,
    came He to a world forlorn,
    the Lord of every nation,
    the Lord of every nation.

2   Cradled in a stall was He
    with sleepy cows and asses;
    but the very beasts could see
    that He all men surpasses,
    that He all men surpasses.

3   Herod then with fear was filled:
    'A Prince,' he said, 'in Jewry!'
    All the little boys he killed
    at Bethlehem in his fury,
    at Bethlehem in his fury.

4   Now may Mary's Son, who came
    so long ago to love us,
    lead us all with hearts aflame
    unto the joys above us,
    unto the joys above us.

5   Alpha and Omega He!
    Let the organ thunder,
    while the choir with peals of glee
    doth rend the air asunder,
    doth rend the air asunder!

264
Fred Kaan
© 1968 Stainer & Bell Ltd

1   **We have a king who rides a donkey,**
    we have a king who rides a donkey,
    we have a king who rides a donkey
    and His name is Jesus.
    Jesus the King is risen,
    Jesus the King is risen,
    Jesus the King is risen
    early in the morning.

2   Trees are waving a royal welcome,
    trees are waving a royal welcome,
    trees are waving a royal welcome
    for the king called Jesus.
    Jesus the King is risen . . .

3   We have a king who cares for people,
    we have a king who cares for people,
    we have a king who cares for people
    and His name is Jesus.
    Jesus the King is risen . . .

4 What shall we do with our life this morning,
what shall we do with our life this morning,
what shall we do with our life this morning?
Give it up in service!
Jesus the King is risen . . .

265 © 1986 Margaret Westworth

1 **We love to praise You, Jesus,**
we love to tell You
that You are Lord, that You are Lord.

2 We love to know You, Jesus,
we love to hear You,
say we are Yours, say we are Yours.

3 We want to thank You, Jesus,
for giving Your life
so we can live, so we can live.

266 Priscilla Jane Owens (1829–1907)
altered © 1986 Horrobin / Leavers

1 **We have heard a joyful sound!**
Jesus saves!
Spread the gladness all around:
Jesus saves!
Words of life for every land
must be sent across the waves;
onward! 'tis our Lord's command:
Jesus saves!

2 Sing above the toils of life:
Jesus saves!
He is with us in the strife:
Jesus saves!
Sing the truth, He died yet lives,
strengthening me through all my days.
Sing in triumph! Life He gives:
Jesus saves!

3 Let the nations hear God's voice:
Jesus saves!
So that they can then rejoice:
Jesus saves!
Shout salvation full and free
that every land may hear God's praise –
this our song of victory:
Jesus saves!

267 Matthias Claudius (1740–1815)
tr. Jane Montgomery Campbell (1817–78)
altered © 1986 Horrobin / Leavers

1 **We plough the fields and scatter**
the good seed on the land,
but it is fed and watered
by God's almighty hand;
He sends the snow in winter,
the warmth to swell the grain,
the breezes and the sunshine
and soft refreshing rain.
All good gifts around us
are sent from heaven above,
then thank the Lord, O thank the Lord,
for all His love.

2 He only is the maker
of all things near and far;
He paints the wayside flower,
He lights the evening star;
the wind and waves obey Him,
by Him the birds are fed;
much more to us, His children,
He gives our daily bread.
All good gifts . . .

3 We thank You then, O Father,
for all things bright and good,
the seed-time and the harvest,
our life, our health, our food.
Accept the gifts we offer
for all Your love imparts;
we come now, Lord, to give You
our humble, thankful hearts.
All good gifts . . .

268 Verses 1 and 2: Ed Baggett
© 1974 Celebration / Kingsway's Thankyou Music
Verse 3 after Thomas Ken (1637–1711)

We really want to thank You, Lord,
we really want to bless Your name:
hallelujah! Jesus is our King!

1 We thank You, Lord, for Your gift to us,
Your life so rich beyond compare,
the gift of Your body here on earth
of which we sing and share.
We really want . . .

2 We thank You, Lord, for our life together,
to live and move in the love of Christ,
Your tenderness which sets us free
to serve You with our lives.
We really want . . .

3 Praise God from whom all blessings flow,
praise Him all creatures here below,
praise Him above, you heavenly host,
praise Father, Son and Holy Ghost.
We really want . . .

269

American folk hymn
Copyright control

**Were you there
when they crucified my Lord?**
Were you there
   when they crucified my Lord?
Oh! Sometimes it causes me to tremble,
   tremble, tremble;
Were you there
   when they crucified my Lord?

Were you there
   when they nailed Him to the tree?
Were you there
   when they nailed Him to the tree?
Oh! Sometimes it causes me to tremble,
   tremble, tremble;
Were you there
   when they nailed Him to the tree?

Were you there
   when they laid Him in the tomb?
Were you there
   when they laid Him in the tomb?
Oh! Sometimes it causes me to tremble,
   tremble, tremble;
Were you there
   when they laid Him in the tomb?

Were you there when God raised Him
   from the dead?
Were you there when God raised Him
   from the dead?
Oh! Sometimes it causes me to tremble,
   tremble, tremble;
Were you there when God raised Him
   from the dead?

70

This song has been withdrawn
for copyright-related reasons

271

John H Hopkins (1820–91)
altered © 1986 Horrobin / Leavers

1 **We three kings of Orient are,**
bearing gifts we travel afar,
field and fountain, moor and mountain,
following yonder star:
*O star of wonder, star of night,
star with royal beauty bright,
westward leading, still proceeding,
guide us to the perfect light.*

2 Born a King on Bethlehem plain,
gold I bring to crown Him again:
King for ever, ceasing never,
over us all to reign.
O star of wonder . . .

3 Frankincense for Jesus have I,
God on earth yet Priest on high;
prayer and praising all men raising:
worship is earth's reply.
O star of wonder . . .

4 Myrrh is mine: its bitter perfume
tells of His death and Calvary's gloom;
sorrowing, sighing, bleeding, dying,
sealed in a stone-cold tomb.
O star of wonder . . .

5 Glorious now, behold Him arise,
King, and God, and sacrifice!
Heaven sings, 'Alleluia!',
'Alleluia!' the earth replies.
O star of wonder . . .

272

Colin Sterne (1862–1926)

1 **We've a story to tell to the nations,**
that shall turn their hearts to the right;
a story of truth and sweetness,
a story of peace and light,
a story of peace and light:
*For the darkness shall turn to dawning,
and the dawning to noon-day bright,
and Christ's great kingdom
   shall come on earth,
the kingdom of love and light.*

2 We've a song to be sung to the nations,
that shall lift their hearts to the Lord;
a song that shall conquer evil,
so love will replace the sword,
so love will replace the sword.
For the darkness . . .

3 We've a message to give to the nations,
that the Lord who's reigning above
has sent us His Son to save us,
and show us that God is love,
and show us that God is love:
For the darkness . . .

4 We've a Saviour to show to the nations,
who the path of sorrow has trod,
that all of the world may listen
and learn of the truth of God,
and learn of the truth of God:
For the darkness . . .

273
Joseph Scriven (1819–86)
altered © 1986 Horrobin / Leavers

1 **What a friend we have in Jesus,**
all our sins and griefs to bear!
What a privilege to carry
everything to God in prayer!
O what peace we often forfeit,
O what needless pain we bear –
all because we do not carry
everything to God in prayer!

2 Have we trials and temptations?
Is there trouble anywhere?
We should never be discouraged:
take it to the Lord in prayer!
Can we find a friend so faithful,
who will all our sorrows share?
Jesus knows our every weakness –
take it to the Lord in prayer!

3 Are we weak and heavy-laden,
cumbered with a load of care?
Jesus only is our refuge!
Take it to the Lord in prayer!
Do your friends despise, forsake you?
Take it to the Lord in prayer!
In His arms He'll take and shield you,
you will find His comfort there.

274
Anon
Copyright control

1 **What a wonderful Saviour is Jesus,**
what a wonderful friend is He,
for He left all the glory of heaven,
came to earth to die on Calvary:
*Sing hosanna, sing hosanna,
sing hosanna to the King of kings!
Sing hosanna, sing hosanna,
sing hosanna to the King.*

2 He arose from the grave, hallelujah!
and He lives never more to die,
at the Father's right hand interceding,
He will hear and heed our faintest cry:
Sing hosanna . . .

3 He is coming some day to receive us,
we'll be caught up to heaven above,
what a joy it will be to behold Him,
sing for ever of His grace and love.
Sing hosanna . . .

275
Sydney Carter
© 1965 Stainer & Bell Ltd

1 **When I needed a neighbour,**
   were you there, were you there?
When I needed a neighbour,
   were you there?
*And the creed and the colour
   and the name won't matter,
were you there?*

2 I was hungry and thirsty,
   were you there, were you there?
I was hungry and thirsty, were you there?
And the creed . . .

3 I was cold, I was naked,
   were you there, were you there?
I was cold, I was naked, were you there?
And the creed . . .

4 When I needed a shelter,
   were you there, were you there?
When I needed a shelter, were you there?
And the creed . . .

5 When I needed a healer, were you there,
   were you there?
When I needed a healer, were you there?
And the creed . . .

6 Wherever you travel, I'll be there,
   I'll be there,
Wherever you travel, I'll be there.
And the creed . . .

276
Spiritual, adapted Peter D Smith
© Stainer & Bell Ltd

1 **When Israel was in Egypt's land,**
let my people go;
oppressed so hard they could not stand,
let my people go.

Go down, Moses, way down in
Egypt's land,
tell old Pharaoh to let my people go.

2 The Lord told Moses what to do,
   let my people go;
   to lead the children of Israel through,
   let my people go.
   Go down . . .

3 Your foes shall not before you stand,
   let my people go;
   and you'll possess fair Canaan's land,
   let my people go.
   Go down . . .

4 O let us from all bondage flee,
   let my people go;
   and let us all in Christ be free,
   let my people go.
   Go down . . .

5 I do believe without a doubt,
   let my people go;
   that a Christian has a right to shout,
   let my people go.
   Go down . . .

277 Isaac Watts (1674–1748)

When I survey the wondrous cross
on which the Prince of glory died,
my richest gain I count but loss,
and pour contempt on all my pride.

Forbid it, Lord, that I should boast,
save in the death of Christ my God:
all the vain things that charm me most,
I sacrifice them to His blood.

See from His head, His hands, His feet,
sorrow and love flow mingled down:
did e'er such love and sorrow meet,
or thorns compose so rich a crown?

Were the whole realm of nature mine,
that were an offering far too small,
love so amazing, so divine,
demands my soul, my life, my all.

278 From the German (19th century)
Edward Caswall (1814–78)
© in this version Jubilate Hymns

1 **When morning gilds the skies,**
   my heart awakening cries:
     May Jesus Christ be praised!
   Alike at work and prayer
   I know my Lord is there:
     May Jesus Christ be praised!

2 When sadness fills my mind
   my strength in Him I find –
     may Jesus Christ be praised!
   When earthly hopes grow dim
   my comfort is in Him –
     may Jesus Christ be praised!

3 The night becomes as day
   when from the heart we say:
     May Jesus Christ be praised!
   The powers of darkness fear,
   when this glad song they hear:
     May Jesus Christ be praised!

4 Be this, while life is mine,
   my canticle divine:
     May Jesus Christ be praised!
   Be this the eternal song
   through all the ages long:
     May Jesus Christ be praised!

279 Norman J Clayton
© Norman Clayton Publishing / Word Music Inc /
Word Music (UK) Ltd / CopyCare Ltd

When the road is rough and steep,
fix your eyes upon Jesus,
He alone has power to keep,
fix your eyes upon Him.
Jesus is a gracious friend,
one on whom you can depend,
He is faithful to the end,
fix your eyes upon Him.

280 © Timothy Dudley-Smith

1 **When the Lord in glory comes,**
   not the trumpets, not the drums,
   not the anthem, not the psalm,
   not the thunder, not the calm,
   not the shout the heavens raise,
   not the chorus, not the praise,

not the silences sublime,
not the sounds of space and time,
but His voice when He appears
shall be music to my ears;
  but His voice when He appears
  shall be music to my ears.

2 When the Lord is seen again,
not the glories of His reign,
not the lightnings through the storm,
not the radiance of His form,
not His pomp and power alone,
not the splendours of His throne,
not His robe and diadems,
not the gold and not the gems,
but His face upon my sight
shall be darkness into light;
  but His face upon my sight
  shall be darkness into light.

3 When the Lord to human eyes
shall bestride our narrow skies,
not the child of humble birth,
not the carpenter of earth,
not the man by all denied,
not the victim crucified,
but the God who died to save,
but the victor of the grave,
He it is to whom I fall,
Jesus Christ, my all in all;
  He it is to whom I fall,
  Jesus Christ, my all in all.

281   James M Black (1856–1938)

1 **When the trumpet of the Lord shall sound,**
  and time shall be no more,
and the morning breaks, eternal,
  bright, and fair;
when the saved of earth shall gather
  over on the other shore,
and the roll is called up yonder, I'll be there.
  When the roll is called up yonder,
  when the roll is called up yonder,
  when the roll is called up yonder,
  when the roll is called up yonder
  I'll be there.

2 On that bright and cloudless morning
  when the dead in Christ shall rise,
and the glory of His resurrection share;
when His chosen ones shall gather
  to their home beyond the skies,
and the roll is called up yonder, I'll be there.
  When the roll is called . . .

3 Let us labour for the Master
  from the dawn till setting sun,
let us talk of all His wondrous love and care;
then when all of life is over,
  and our work on earth is done,
and the roll is called up yonder, I'll be there.
  When the roll is called . . .

282   Anon
Copyright control

Wherever I am, I'll praise Him,
whenever I can, I'll praise Him;
for His love surrounds me like a sea;
I'll praise the name of Jesus,
lift up the name of Jesus,
for the name of Jesus lifted me.

283   © 1986 Margaret Westworth

1 **Wherever I am I will praise You, Lord,**
praise You, Lord.
Wherever I am
Your Spirit fills my life with song.

2 Whenever I can I will tell You, Lord,
I love You.
Wherever I am
Your Spirit fills my heart with love.

3 Wherever I go I will serve You, Lord,
serve You, Lord.
Wherever I am
Your Spirit fills my life with power.

4 Whatever I do I will need You, Lord,
need You, Lord.
Wherever I am
Your Spirit lives Your life through me.

284   Graham Kendrick
© 1986 Kingsway's Thankyou Music

1 **Whether you're one or whether you're two**
or three or four or five,
six or seven or eight or nine,
it's good to be alive.
It really doesn't matter how old you are,
Jesus loves you whoever you are.
  La, la, la, la, la, la, la, la, la,
  Jesus loves us all.
  La, la, la, la, la, la, la, la, la,
  Jesus loves us all.

Whether you're big or whether you're small
or somewhere in between,
first in the class or middle or last,
we're all the same to Him.
It really doesn't matter how clever you are,
Jesus loves you whoever you are.
La, la, la, la . . .

285 Nahum Tate (1652–1715)

**While shepherds watched
their flocks by night,**
all seated on the ground,
the angel of the Lord came down
and glory shone around.

'Fear not,' said he – for mighty dread
had seized their troubled mind –
'Glad tidings of great joy I bring
to you and all mankind:

'To you in David's town this day
is born of David's line,
a Saviour, who is Christ the Lord.
And this shall be the sign:

'The heavenly babe you there shall find
to human view displayed,
all meanly wrapped in swaddling bands,
and in a manger laid.'

Thus spake the angel; and forthwith
appeared a shining throng
of angels praising God, who thus
addressed their joyful song:

'All glory be to God on high,
and to the earth be peace;
goodwill henceforth from heaven to men
begin and never cease!'

286 Betty Lou Mills and Russell J Mills
© 1968 B L Mills and R J Mills /
Copyright control

**Who took fish and bread,
hungry people fed?**
Who changed water into wine?
Who made well the sick,
who made see the blind?
Who touched earth with feet divine?
Only Jesus, only Jesus,
only He has done this:
Who made live the dead?
Truth and kindness spread?
Only Jesus did all this.

2 Who walked dusty road?
Cared for young and old?
Who sat children on His knee?
Who spoke words so wise?
Filled men with surprise?
Who gave all but charged no fee?
Only Jesus, only Jesus,
only He has done this:
Who in death and grief
spoke peace to a thief?
Only Jesus did all this.

3 Who soared through the air?
Joined His Father there?
He has you and me in view:
He who this has done is God's only Son,
and He's interested in you.
Only Jesus, only Jesus,
only He has done this:
He can change a heart,
give a fresh new start,
only He can do all this.

287 Frances Ridley Havergal (1836–79)
altered © 1986 Horrobin / Leavers

1 **Who is on the Lord's side?**
Who will serve the King?
Who will be His helpers
other lives to bring?
Who will leave the world's side?
Who will face the foe?
Who is on the Lord's side?
Who for Him will go?
By His call of mercy,
now our lives we bring,
we are on the Lord's side;
Jesus, He's our King.

2 Fierce may be the conflict,
strong may be the foe,
but the King's own army
none can overthrow.
Round His standard ranging,
victory is secure,
for His truth unchanging
makes the triumph sure.
Joyfully enlisting,
now our lives we bring,
we are on the Lord's side;
Jesus, He's our King.

3 Chosen to be soldiers
in an alien land,
chosen, called, and faithful,
for our captain's band;

in the service royal
let us not grow cold;
let us be right loyal,
noble, true and bold.
Master, You will keep us,
serving You we sing:
'Always on the Lord's side,
Jesus, always King!'

288 J A P Booth
© Paul Booth

1 **Who put the colours in the rainbow?**
Who put the salt into the sea?
Who put the cold into the snowflake?
Who made you and me?
Who put the hump upon the camel?
Who put the neck on the giraffe?
Who put the tail upon the monkey?
Who made hyenas laugh?
Who made whales and snails and quails?
Who made hogs and dogs and frogs?
Who made bats and rats and cats?
Who made everything?

2 Who put the gold into the sunshine?
Who put the sparkle in the stars?
Who put the silver in the moonlight?
Who made Earth and Mars?
Who put the scent into the roses?
Who taught the honey bee to dance?
Who put the tree inside the acorn?
It surely can't be chance!
Who made seas and leaves and trees?
Who made snow and winds that blow?
Who made streams and rivers flow?
God made all of these!

289 © Annie Bush

Who's the king of the jungle?
Who's the king of the sea?
Who's the king of the universe
and who's the king of me?
I'll tell you J-E-S-U-S is,
He's the king of me,
He's the king of the universe,
the jungle and the sea.

290 Priscilla Jane Owens (1829–1907)

1 **Will your anchor hold in the storms of life,**
when the clouds unfold their wings of strife?
When the strong tides lift,
    and the cables strain,
will your anchor drift, or firm remain?
*We have an anchor that keeps the soul
steadfast and sure while the billows roll;
fastened to the rock which cannot move,
grounded firm and deep
in the Saviour's love!*

2 Will your anchor hold in the straits of fear,
when the breakers roar and the reef is near?
While the surges rage,
    and the wild winds blow,
shall the angry waves then your life o'erflow?
We have an anchor . . .

3 Will your anchor hold in the floods of death,
when the waters cold chill your final breath?
On the rising tide you can never fail,
while your anchor holds within the veil.
We have an anchor . . .

4 Will your eyes behold
    through the morning light,
the city of gold and the harbour bright?
Will you anchor safe by the heavenly shore,
when life's storms are past for evermore?
We have an anchor . . .

291 Anon
Copyright control

**With Jesus in the boat
    we can smile at the storm,**
smile at the storm, smile at the storm,
with Jesus in the boat
    we can smile at the storm
as we go sailing home.
Sailing, sailing home,
sailing, sailing home,
with Jesus in the boat
    we can smile at the storm
as we go sailing home.

292
C Austin Miles (1865–1946)
© 1917, 1945 The Rodeheaver Co / Word Music Inc /
Word Music (UK) / CopyCare Ltd

Wide, wide as the ocean,
  high as the heaven above,
deep, deep as the deepest sea
  is my Saviour's love.
I, though so unworthy,
  still am a child of His care,
for His word teaches me that His love
  reaches me everywhere.

93
John Hampden Gurney (1802–1862)

Yes, God is good – in earth and sky,
from ocean depths and spreading wood,
ten thousand voices seem to cry:
'God made us all, and God is good!'

The sun that keeps his trackless way,
and downward pours his golden flood,
night's sparkling hosts, all seem to say
in accents clear that God is good.

The joyful birds prolong the strain,
their song with every spring renewed;
the air we breathe, and falling rain,
each softly whispers: 'God is good!'

I hear it in the rushing breeze;
the hills that have for ages stood,
the echoing sky and roaring seas,
all swell the chorus: 'God is good!'

Yes, God is good, all nature says,
by God's own hand with speech endued;
and man, in louder notes of praise,
should sing for joy that God is good.

For all Your gifts we bless You, Lord,
but chiefly for our heavenly food,
Your pardoning grace,
    Your quickening word,
these prompt our song, that God is good.

94
Albert B Simpson (1843–1919)

Yesterday, today, for ever,
Jesus is the same;
all may change, but Jesus never,
glory to His name!
Glory to His name!
Glory to His name!
All may change, but Jesus never,
glory to His name!

295
Georgian Banov
© 1978 Birdwing Music / Careers BMG Music /
Candle Co Music / Alliance Media Ltd / CopyCare Ltd

1 **Your ways are higher than mine,**
   Your ways are higher than mine,
   Your ways are higher than mine,
   much higher.
   Your ways are higher than mine,
   Your ways are higher than mine,
   Your ways are higher than mine,
   much higher.
   Higher, higher, much much higher,
   higher, higher, much higher.
   Higher, higher, much much higher,
   higher, higher, much higher.

2 Your thoughts are wiser . . .

3 Your strength is greater . . .

   Hallelujah, hallelujah,
   hallelujah, hallelu.
   Hallelujah, hallelujah,
   hallelujah, hallelu.

296
Mavis Ford
© 1978 Springtide / Word Music (UK) /
CopyCare Ltd

You are the King of glory,
You are the Prince of peace,
You are the Lord of heaven and earth,
You're the Son of righteousness.
Angels bow down before You,
worship and adore,
for You have the words of eternal life,
You are Jesus Christ the Lord.
Hosanna to the Son of David!
Hosanna to the King of kings!
Glory in the highest heaven,
for Jesus the Messiah reigns!

297
John Gowans
© 1970 Salvationist Publishing and Supplies Ltd /
CopyCare Ltd

1 **You can't stop rain from falling down,**
   prevent the sun from shining,
   you can't stop spring from coming in,
   or winter from resigning,
   or still the waves or stay the winds,
   or keep the day from dawning;
   you can't stop God from loving you,
   His love is new each morning.

2 You can't stop ice from being cold,
you can't stop fire from burning,
or hold the tide that's going out,
delay its sure returning,
or halt the progress of the years,
the flight of fame and fashion;
you can't stop God from loving you,
His nature is compassion.

3 You can't stop God from loving you,
though you may disobey Him.
You can't stop God from loving you,
however you betray Him.
From love like this no power on earth
the human heart can sever.
You can't stop God from loving you,
not God, not now, not ever.

298 Edward Hayes Plumptre (1821–91)

1 **Your hand, O God, has guided**
Your flock, from age to age;
Your faithfulness is written
on history's open page;
our fathers knew Your goodness,
and we their deeds record;
and both to this bear witness:
One Church, one faith, one Lord.

2 Your heralds brought the gospel
to greatest as to least;
they summoned men to hasten
and share the great King's feast;
and this was all their teaching
in every deed and word;
to all alike proclaiming:
One Church, one faith, one Lord.

3 Through many days of darkness,
through many scenes of strife,
the faithful few fought bravely
to guard the nation's life.
Their gospel of redemption,
sin pardoned, man restored,
was all in this enfolded:
One Church, one faith, one Lord.

4 Your mercy will not fail us,
nor leave Your work undone;
with Your right hand to help us,
the victory shall be won;
and then by earth and heaven
Your name shall be adored,
and this shall be their anthem:
One Church, one faith, one Lord.

299 Edmond Budry (1854–1932)
tr. R Birch Hoyle (1875–1939)
© in this version Jubilate Hymns

1 **Yours be the glory, risen, conquering Son**
endless is the victory over death You won;
angels robed in splendour
rolled the stone away,
kept the folded grave-clothes
where Your body lay.
Yours be the glory, risen, conquering Son,
endless is the victory over death You won.

2 See! Jesus meets us, risen from the tomb;
lovingly He greets us,
scatters fear and gloom;
let the Church with gladness
hymns of triumph sing,
for her Lord is living; death has lost its sting
Yours be the glory . . .

3 No more we doubt You,
glorious Prince of life;
what is life without You? Aid us in our strife;
make us more than conquerors,
through Your deathless love:
bring us safe through Jordan
to Your home above.
Yours be the glory . . .

300 Anon
Copyright control

Zacchaeus was a very little man,
and a very little man was he.
He climbed up into a sycamore tree
for the Saviour he wanted to see.
And when the Saviour passed that way
He looked into the tree
and said, 'Now, Zacchaeus, you come dow
for I'm coming to your house to tea.'

301 © 1986 Peter Horrobin

1 **Lord, we ask now to receive**
Your blessing,
Lord, we ask now to receive Your love,
Come, we pray, come, we pray
and lead us hour by hour.
Bless, we ask, our friends and
close relations,
let them feel Your touch of loving power.

2 Lord, we trust You to give us Your blessing,
   Lord, we trust You to give us Your love.
   As we give, as we give
   our lives afresh to You.
   Take, we ask, all that we have and are, Lord,
   let them now be used in service true.

3 Lord, we give to others now Your blessing,
   Lord, we give to others now Your love.
   As we share, as we share
   with them the life You've given.
   Yes, we will, in harmony with You, Lord,
   let them see in us a touch of heaven.

302
Paul Field

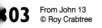

1 **A naggy mum, a grumpy dad,**
     a brother who's a pain.
   A sister who takes toys and never
        gives them back again.
   All the same, all the same,
   in sunshine and in rain.
   No matter who we are, you know,
   God loves us all the same.

2 An auntie who cooks sprouts for tea
        and makes you eat them all.
   A grandad who tells terrible jokes
        and drives you up the wall.
   All the same . . .

3 An uncle who forgets about your birthday
        when it comes.
   A teacher who gets cross with you
        and makes you do more sums.
   All the same . . .

303
From John 13

A new commandment that I give to you,
is to love one another as I have loved you,
is to love one another as I have loved you.

By this shall all men know
     that you are My disciples,
if you have love one for another;
by this shall all men know
     that you are My disciples,
if you have love one for another.

304

1 **A purple robe, a crown of thorn,**
   a reed in His right hand;
   before the soldiers' spite and scorn
   I see my Saviour stand.

2 He bears between the Roman guard
   the weight of all our woe;
   a stumbling figure bowed and scarred
   I see my Saviour go.

3 Fast to the cross's spreading span,
   high in the sunlit air,
   all the unnumbered sins of man
   I see my Saviour bear.

4 He hangs, by whom the world was made,
   beneath the darkened sky;
   the everlasting ransom paid,
   I see my Saviour die.

5 He shares on high His Father's throne,
   who once in mercy came;
   for all His love to sinners shown
   I sing my Saviour's name.

305

1 **A special star is in the sky**
   to lead the way (to lead the way);
   a tiny stable cold and lonely
   where they can stay (where they can stay).
   But our hearts have been warm,
   since the day Jesus Christ was born,
   and that's the way it shall stay,
   because He is the way,
   the truth and the life,
   (the truth and the life).

2 The shepherds left their flocks behind
   to see the Babe (to see the Babe);
   the angel told them to bring a gift so
   a lamb they gave (a lamb they gave).
   But our hearts . . .

3 The wise men came from lands afar,
   on camels they rode, (on camels they rode);
   the gifts they offered were frankincense,
   myrrh and gold (myrrh and gold).
   But our hearts . . .

306 Paul Field
© 1991 Daybreak Music Ltd

1 **A wiggly waggly worm,**
   a slippery slimy slug,
   a creepy crawly buzzy thing,
   a tickly wickly bug.
   Of all the things to be, I'm happy that I'm me.
   Thank you, Lord, I'm happy that I'm me.

   I'm happy that I'm me, happy that I'm me.
   There's no-one else in all the world
   that I would rather be.
   A wiggly waggly worm, a slippery slimy slug,
   a creepy crawly buzzy thing,
   a tickly wickly bug.

2 A prickly porcupine, a clumsy kangaroo,
   A croaky frog, a hairy hog,
   a monkey in a zoo.
   Of all the things to be, I'm happy that I'm me.
   Thank you, Lord, I'm happy that I'm me.

   I'm happy that I'm me, happy that I'm me.
   There's no-one else in all the world
   that I would rather be.
   A prickly porcupine, a clumsy kangaroo,
   a croaky frog, a hairy hog,
   a monkey in a zoo.

307 Paul Field and Ralph Chambers
© 1991 Daybreak Music Ltd

All you have to do is to ask the Lord
to forgive the wrong things you have done.
Tell Him that you're sorry you have hurt Him,
and then believe that Jesus is God's Son.
He died on the cross to be your Saviour,
rose from the dead to be your special friend.
Ask Him in your heart,
   make a brand new start.
Love and serve Him till your life shall end.

308 Anon
Copyright control

1 **Alleluia. (8 times)**

2 How I love Him . . .

3 Blessèd Jesus . . .

4 My Redeemer . . .

5 Jesus, Master . . .

6 Alleluia . . .

309 Kathie Hill and Janet McMahan
© 1983, 1986 John T Benson Co /
Fine Balance Music/CopyCare Ltd

Are you humbly grateful
or grumbly hateful?
What's your attitude?
Do you grumble and groan,
or let it be known
you're grateful for all
God's done for you?

1 When Jonah found himself
   in the belly of a whale,
   did he cause a riot inside?
   No!
   He headed for shore
   with his message from God
   and thanked the Lord
   for his free ride.
   Phew!
   Are you humbly grateful . . .

2 When Noah found himself
   in the floating zoo,
   did he ever try to jump ship?
   No!
   For forty long days
   and for forty long nights
   he cleared the deck
   on that long trip!
   Phew!
   Are you humbly grateful . . .

   Which one are you?
   Spoken Which one are you?

310 Peter and Hanneke Jacobs
© 1988 Maranatha! Music / CopyCare Ltd

And we know that all things,
all things, all things work together for good,
yes, we know that all things,
all things, all things work together for good!
To them that love the Lord,
to them that love the Lord,
to them that love the Lord,
and are called according to His purpose.
And we know that all things,
all things, all things work together for good,
yes, we know that all things,
all things, all things work together for good.
Romans eight, verse twenty-eight.

311

1 **At harvest time we celebrate**
God's gift to us of food and drink.
We thank Him for the care He's shown
for farmers and the seeds they've sown.
   Praise the Lord! Praise the Lord!
   Praise the Lord! Praise the Lord!
   Praise the Lord! Praise the Lord!
   Thank Him for harvest.

2 God's watched the fields
      through day and night,
He's given the seeds both dark and light.
He's watered them with fresh cool rain
and now there's fields and fields of grain.
   Praise the Lord . . .

3 God helps the farmers cut the corn,
He keeps the weather dry and warm,
until it's baled and brought inside,
before the start of wintertide.
   Praise the Lord . . .

Now once the crops are in their barns
there's work to do still on the farms.
It's time to put the crops to use
to make the different kinds of foods.
   Praise the Lord . . .

At harvest time we celebrate
God's gifts to us of food and drink.
Let's sing and clap to show our thanks
for all the care God takes of us.
   Praise the Lord . . .
   Praise the Lord . . .

312

Be careful, little hands, what you do,
be careful, little hands, what you do.
There's a Father up above who is
      looking down in love,
so be careful, little hands, what you do.

13

Born in the night,
   Mary's child,
a long way from Your home:
coming in need,
   Mary's child,
born in a borrowed room.

2 Clear shining light,
   Mary's child,
Your face lights up our way:
light of the world,
   Mary's child,
dawn on our darkened day.

3 Truth of our life,
   Mary's child,
You tell us God is good:
prove it is true,
   Mary's child,
go to Your cross of wood.

4 Hope of the world,
   Mary's child,
You're coming soon to reign:
King of the earth,
   Mary's child,
walk in our streets again.

314

1 **Be holy in all that you do,**
be holy in all that you do,
be holy in all that you do today,
be holy in all that you do,
you are a chosen people,
be holy in all that you do,
you are a chosen people,
be holy in all that you do.

2 Be holy in all that you say . . .

3 Be holy in all that you think . . .

4 Be holy in all that you are . . .

315

   Bring your Christingle
   with gladness and joy!
   Sing praise to God who gave us His Son;
   so give Him, give Him your love.

LEADER
1 Here is an orange –
ALL
An orange as round as the world
      that God made.
   Bring your Christingle . . .

LEADER
2 Here is a candle –
ALL
A candle for Jesus, the Light of the world,
an orange as round as the world
    that God made;
    Bring your Christingle . . .

LEADER
3 Here is red ribbon –
ALL
Red ribbon reminds us Christ died for us all;
a candle for Jesus, the Light of the world;
an orange as round as the world
    that God made;
    Bring your Christingle . . .

LEADER
4 Here are the fruits –
ALL
The fruits of the earth God has given
    us to share;
red ribbon reminds us Christ died for us all;
a candle for Jesus, the Light of the world;
an orange as round as the world
    that God made;
    Bring your Christingle . . .

316 © Geoffrey Marshall-Taylor / Jubilate Hymns

1 **Can you be sure that the rain will fall?**
Can you be sure that birds will fly?
Can you be sure that rivers will flow?
Or that the sun will light the sky?
God has promised.
God never breaks a promise He makes.
His word is always true.

2 Can you be sure that the tide will turn?
Can you be sure that grass will grow?
Can you be sure that night will come,
or that the sun will melt the snow?
God has promised . . .

3 You can be sure that God is near;
you can be sure He won't let you down;
you can be sure He'll always hear;
and that He's given Jesus, His Son.
God has promised . . .

317 Paul Field
© 1991 Daybreak Music

1 **Can you count the stars shining**
   in the sky?
Can you hold the moonlight in your hand?
Can you stop the waves rolling
   on the shore?
Or find the place where rainbows
   meet the land?
I've got a friend, who knows how
   all these things are done,
Jesus, Lord of all, God's only Son.

2 Up in outer space, planets spinning round,
millions more than we can ever see.
It's hard to understand how God,
   who made it all,
still cares about someone like you and me.
I've got a friend . . .

318 Jeanette Smart
© Lillenas Publishing Co / CopyCare Ltd

1 **Can you imagine how it feels to know**
the God who made the earth
   and sky and sea?
When He created all the universe,
His mighty plan included you and me.
Well, this experience is not imagination;
it's a fact, oh yes, it's true.
And I just can't keep it to myself;
I'll pass it on to you.

2 Can you imagine how it feels to have
a Friend who never slumbers, never sleeps?
Can you believe that when He comes into
your heart and says He'll live there,
   it's for keeps?
Well, this experience is not imagination;
it's a fact, oh yes, it's true.
And I just can't keep it to myself;
I'll pass it on to you,
and you, and you, and you.

319 © Timothy Dudley-Smith

1 **Christ be my leader by night as by day;**
safe through the darkness, for He is the way
Gladly I follow, my future His care;
darkness is daylight when Jesus is there.

Christ be my teacher in age as in youth,
drifting or doubting, for He is the truth.
Grant me to trust Him,
    though shifting as sand;
doubt cannot daunt me, in Jesus I stand.

Christ be my Saviour in calm as in strife;
death cannot hold me, for He is the life.
Not darkness nor doubting
    nor sin and its stain
can touch my salvation: with Jesus I reign.

20 Joe E Parks
© Singspiration Music / Fine Balance Music /
CopyCare Ltd

Children, join the celebration
on this happy Easter day;
Christ the Lord is risen as He said!
Mary on that early morning
heard the angel gladly say:
'Jesus lives – He is no longer dead!'

Praise Him now with songs of gladness,
sing triumphant hymns of praise:
Christ the Lord is risen as He said!
Children, join the celebration,
with the hosts of heaven say:
'Jesus Christ, our Saviour, lives today!'

21 Ernie and Debbie Rettino
© Maranatha! Music / CopyCare Ltd

Christmas is a time, Christmas is a time,
Christmas is a time to love.
Christmas is a time, Christmas is a time,
Christmas is a time to love.

We often start to worry, and people get upset
if things don't all go right on Christmas day.
What we should remember in all the push
    and shove,
is Christmas is a time of love.

Christmas is a time, Christmas is a time,
Christmas is a time to love.
Christmas is a time, Christmas is a time,
Christmas is a time to love.

322 Jimmy and Carol Owens
© 1980 Bud John Songs / Alliance Media Ltd /
CopyCare Ltd

**Christmas isn't Christmas
    till it happens in your heart;**
somewhere deep inside you
    is where Christmas really starts.
So give your heart to Jesus;
    you'll discover when you do
that it's Christmas, really Christmas for you.

Jesus brings warmth like a winter fire,
a light like a candle's glow.
He's waiting now to come inside
as He did so long ago.
Jesus brings gifts of truth and life,
and makes them bloom and grow.
So welcome Him with a song of joy,
and when He comes, you'll know,

that Christmas isn't Christmas
    till it happens in your heart;
somewhere deep inside you
    is where Christmas really starts.
So give your heart to Jesus;
    you'll discover when you do
that it's Christmas, really Christmas;
Christmas, really Christmas for you.

323 Valerie Collison
© 1972 High-Fye Music Ltd

Come and join the celebration,
it's a very special day;
come and share our jubilation,
there's a new King born today!

1 See the shepherds
   hurry down to Bethlehem;
   gaze in wonder
   at the Son of God who lay before them.
   Come and join . . .

2 Wise men journey,
   led to worship by a star;
   kneel in homage,
   bringing precious gifts from lands afar, so
   Come and join . . .

3 'God is with us,'
   round the world the message bring;
   He is with us,
   'Welcome!' all the bells on earth are pealing.
   Come and join . . .

324 From Psalm 95
© 1987 Ruth Hooke

BOYS **Come, let us sing
for joy to the Lord.**

GIRLS Come, let us sing for joy to the Lord.

BOYS We will sing, we will sing, we will sing.

GIRLS We will sing, we will sing, we will sing.

BOYS Let us shout aloud
to the rock of our salvation.

GIRLS Let us shout aloud
to the rock of our salvation.

BOYS We will shout! We will shout!
We will shout!

GIRLS We will shout! We will shout!
We will shout!

ALL For the Lord is the great God,
the great King above all gods.

BOYS Splendour and majesty,

GIRLS splendour and majesty,

BOYS are before Him,

GIRLS are before Him.

BOYS Strength and glory,

GIRLS strength and glory,

ALL are in His sanctuary.

326 © Carolyn Keats

*Counting, counting, one, two, three,
clap my hands and
sing for joy, for
God made ME!
Three, four, five, six,
and number seven too;
shout it loud, make
sure you're heard, for
God made YOU!*

1 I have ten toes, ten fingers,
two legs on which I stand,
an arm on either side of me,
at the end of each a hand;
a right ear and a left ear,
a head to shake and nod,
two eyes, one nose, a mouth, a voice
to whisper or to SHOUT!
Counting, counting . . .

2 God made me very different
from everyone I see,
my size and shape and colour,
He chose it carefully.
God is so very clever
He made the whole world too;
He put the life in everything
including me and you.
Counting, counting . . .

325 Patricia Morgan and Dave Bankhead
© 1984 Kingsway's Thankyou Music

Come on and celebrate!
His gift of love we will celebrate –
the Son of God, who loved us
and gave us life.

We'll shout Your praise, O King:
You give us joy nothing else can bring;
we'll give to You our offering
in celebration praise.

Come on and celebrate, celebrate,
celebrate and sing,
celebrate and sing to the King.
Come on and celebrate, celebrate,
celebrate and sing,
celebrate and sing to the King!

327 Ian White
© Little Misty Music Ltd

1 **Crackers and turkeys and pudding
and cream,**
toys in the windows that I've never seen.
This is the Christmas that everyone sees,
but Christmas means more to me.
*It's somebody's birthday I won't forget,
as I open the things that I get.
I'll remember the inn and the stable
so bare,
and Jesus who once lay there.*

2 Everyone's out shopping late every night,
for candles and presents and
Christmas tree lights.
This is the Christmas that everyone sees,
but Christmas means more to me.
It's somebody's birthday . . .

3 Christmas morning, the start of the day,
there's presents to open and new games
to play.
This is the Christmas that everyone sees,
but Christmas means more to me.
It's somebody's birthday . . .

330 Sam Horner
© 1991 Daybreak Music

1 **Even if I don't like the way things
went today,**
even if I'm feeling down,
I'll praise You anyway.
If I'm feeling lonely, if I'm feeling bad,
I'll think about the things You've done,
and even when I'm sad:
I will worship You in spirit and in truth,
I will worship You in spirit and in truth,
I will worship You in spirit and in truth,
I will worship You in spirit and in truth.

2 When my life is going great,
when everything is right,
help me not to forget You, Lord,
or keep You out of sight.
I don't want to leave You out,
not even for a day,
I want to see Your hand at work
and hear the words You say.
I will worship You . . .

328 Ralph Chambers
© 1991 Daybreak Music Ltd

Don't know much about the ozone layer,
rain forests seem miles away.
But each of us can be a player,
fight to save the world God has made.
This is God's world.
This is God's world,
and you're a member of the human race.
This is God's world.
This is God's world.
Let's try to make it a better place.

329 Frances Towle Rath
© 1974 Child Evangelism Fellowship Inc

Did you ever talk to God above?
Tell Him that you need a friend to love?
Pray in Jesus' name believing
that God answers prayer?

Have you told Him all your cares and woes?
Every tiny little fear He knows.
You can know He'll always hear
and He will answer prayer.

You can whisper in a crowd to Him.
You can cry when you're alone to Him.
You don't have to pray out loud to Him;
He knows your thoughts.

On a lofty mountain peak, He's there.
In a meadow by a stream, He's there.
Anywhere on earth you go
He's been there from the start.

Find the answer in His word; it's true.
You'll be strong because He walks with you.
By His faithfulness He'll change you too.
God answers prayer.

331 © 1992 Greg Leavers

1 **Every day, if you go astray,**
stop! and turn around.
Then don't worry if you've said sorry,
stop! and turn around.
When we come to Jesus
He says He'll forgive us,
for He cares about us.
This is what He promises.
When we come to Jesus
He says He'll forgive us
for He cares about us all.

2 Every day as we walk God's way
stop! and praise the Lord.
He will change us for He's living in us,
stop! and praise the Lord.
Jesus, You forgive us,
then bring Your life to us
through Your Holy Spirit.
This is what You promise us.
Jesus, You forgive us,
then bring Your life to us
through Your Spirit in our lives.

3 Jesus, Saviour, Redeemer and King,
   let's go! and live for Him.
   Son of God, our helper and friend,
   go! and live for Him.
   Jesus, how we thank You,
   Jesus, how we love You,
   Jesus, help us trust You
   till the day You come again.
   Jesus, how we thank You,
   Jesus, how we love You,
   Jesus, help us trust You more.

2 Jump up if you've ridden a bike. (*Jump*)
   Wave your arms if you've flown in a plane.
   (*Wave*)
   Clap your hands if you've been in a car.
   (*Clap*)
   Stamp your feet if you've been on a train.
   (*Stamp*)
   Everyone in the whole wide world . . .

334
Ian White
© Little Misty Music Ltd

Everywhere He walks with me,
and through prayer He talks with me.
He has cared enough for me,
to die to set me free.

1 Since then you have been raised with Christ,
   set your hearts on things above.
   Where Christ is seated at God's right hand,
   set your minds on things above.
   Everywhere He walks with me . . .

2 Put to death whatever is sin,
   rid yourselves of all these things.
   You have been renewed in the Lord,
   and He is all, and is in all.
   Everywhere He walks with me . . .

3 Let His peace now rule in your hearts.
   Let His word be rich in you.
   Sing psalms and hymns with thanks to God,
   praise Him in all that you do.
   Everywhere He walks with me . . .

332
© 1992 Greg Leavers

Everybody join in singing this song,
thanking God for all the good things
   He's done:
showing love for us through Jesus
   His Son,
good and bad and the weak and strong.
Young and old all can sing along;
come on, everybody sing this song.

1 Thank God for the gift of life.
   Thank Him for His care.
   When our lives then get messed up,
   He'll clear out the bad things there.
   Everybody join in singing . . .

2 In our lives God wants to live,
   make His presence known.
   If we're sorry He'll forgive,
   then our hearts can be His home.
   Everybody join in singing . . .

333
Derek and Jackie Llewellyn
© 1990 Sea Dream Music

Everyone in the whole wide world
matters to our friend Jesus.
Everyone, every boy or girl,
we all matter to Him.

1 Jump up if you're wearing red. (*Jump up*)
   Wave your arms if you're wearing blue.
   (*Wave*)
   Clap your hands if you're wearing green.
   (*Clap*)
   Stamp your feet if you're wearing shoes.
   (*Stamp*)
   Everyone in the whole wide world . . .

335
© 1990 Greg Leavers

1 **Father, be with *her/his/their family,**
   as they cry with sadness today.
   Aching hearts feeling such a loss:
   may they know Your love.

2 Comfort them with Your love, O Lord,
   as they try to understand
   why You called *her/him/them
       to be with You;
   may they know Your peace.

* (Use the relevant word or use the child's name)

336

1 **Father, for our friends we pray,**
please be near to them today;
in their sadness, through their tears,
may they know Your peace.

2 Now that he/she is by Your side
comfort friends when they ask why
their dear loved one had to die;
may they know Your love.

3 Though part of their lives has gone,
give them strength to carry on.
As they face the days to come,
may they know Your care.

337

Father God, I wonder
how I managed to exist
without the knowledge
of Your parenthood
and Your loving care.
But now I am Your son,
I am adopted in Your family,
and I can never be alone
'cause, Father God,
You're there beside me.

I will sing Your praises,
I will sing Your praises,
I will sing Your praises for evermore.
I will sing Your praises,
I will sing Your praises,
I will sing Your praises for evermore.

38

**Father, Your word is like a
light in the darkness.**
Father, Your word is like a
sharp, sharp sword.
Father, Your word is like a
stream in the desert.
There's nothing that compares
with the wisdom of Your word.

339

1 **Fill your hearts with joy and gladness,**
sing and praise your God and mine!
Great the Lord in love and wisdom,
might and majesty divine!
He who framed the starry heavens
knows and names them as they shine.

2 Praise the Lord, His people, praise Him!
wounded souls His comfort know;
those who fear Him find His mercies,
peace for pain and joy for woe;
humble hearts are high exalted,
human pride and power laid low.

3 Praise the Lord for times and seasons,
cloud and sunshine, wind and rain;
spring to melt the snows of winter
till the waters flow again;
grass upon the mountain pastures,
golden valleys thick with grain.

4 Fill your hearts with joy and gladness,
peace and plenty crown your days;
love His laws, declare His judgements,
walk in all His words and ways;
He the Lord and we His children –
praise the Lord, all people, praise!

340

**For the foolishness of God is wiser
than man's wisdom,**
and the weakness of God is stronger
than man's strength.
For the foolishness of God is wiser
than man's wisdom,
and the weakness of God is stronger
than man's strength.
For the foolishness of God is wiser
than man's wisdom,
and the weakness of God is stronger
than man's strength.
For the foolishness of God is wiser
than man's wisdom,
and the weakness of God is stronger
than man's strength.

God knows all about the world,
 the things we cannot see,
the things that we don't understand
 that baffle you and me.
His strength is never-ending
 and we are weak and small.
His hand supports the universe
 and He is in control.

For the foolishness of God . . .

341 Graham Kendrick
© 1983 Kingsway's Thankyou Music

1 **From heaven You came, helpless babe,**
entered our world, Your glory veiled,
not to be served but to serve,
and give Your life that we might live.
 This is our God, the Servant King,
 He calls us now to follow Him,
 to bring our lives as a daily offering
 of worship to the Servant King.

2 There in the garden of tears
my heavy load He chose to bear;
His heart with sorrow was torn,
'Yet not my will but yours,' He said.
 This is our God . . .

3 Come see His hands and His feet,
the scars that speak of sacrifice,
hands that flung stars into space
to cruel nails surrendered.
 This is our God . . .

4 So let us learn how to serve
and in our lives enthrone Him,
each other's needs to prefer,
for it is Christ we're serving.
 This is our God . . .

342 © 1990 Greg Leavers

From my knees to my nose,
from my head to my toes,
does God know all about me?
If I'm happy or sad,
if I'm good or I'm bad,
does God know all about me?
The answer is yes
and He loves me the best,
though He knows everything about me.
The answer is yes
and He loves me the best,
and He knows that my name is . . .
 (*shout name*)

343 C Powell and K Wood
© 1991 Sea Dream Music

Get up out of bed,
have a yawn and scratch your head
and say, 'Thank you, it's a brand new day.'

Stretch out, touch your toes,
blink your eyes and blow your nose
and say, 'Thank you, it's a brand new day.'

Actions for the chorus:
Crouch down and jump up.
Hand over mouth, scratch head.
Lift right palm upwards on the word 'Thank',
 lift left palm on the word 'you'.
Arms out, bend over, touch your toes.
Clench fists and eyes, then open, hand to nose.
As before.

1 Jesus taught us all to go His way.
Get out of bed and go with Him today.
 Get up out of bed . . .

2 Jesus showed us that He can make us new.
Get out of bed and ask Him what to do.
 Get up out of bed . . .

3 Jesus loves us all just like He said.
Get out of bed and shake your sleepy head.
 Get up out of bed . . .

344 Malcolm Sargent (1895–1967)
© Oxford University Press
in this version Word & Music / Jubilate Hymns

1 **Girls and boys, leave your toys,**
 make no noise,
kneel at His crib and worship Him.
For this shrine, Child divine, is the sign
our Saviour's here.
 Alleluia, the church bells ring.
 'Alleluia!' the angels sing,
 alleluia from everything –
 all must draw near!

2 On that day, far away, Jesus lay –
angels were watching round His head.
Holy Child, mother mild, undefiled,
we sing Your praise.
 Alleluia . . .
 our hearts we raise.

3 Shepherds came at the fame of Your name,
angels their guide to Bethlehem;
in that place, saw Your face filled with grace
stood at Your door.
 Alleluia . . .
 love evermore.

345
Janet Morgan
© 1989 Sea Dream Music

Give thanks to the Lord for He is good.
Give thanks to the Lord for ever.
Give thanks to the Lord for He is good.

1 When you jump out of bed
and you touch your toes,
when you brush your teeth
and put on your clothes,
Give thanks . . .

2 When you eat your dinner
and you're all full up,
when your Mum says (*Name*)
and you help wash up,
Give thanks . . .

3 When you stretch up high
and you touch the ground,
when you stretch out wide
and you turn around,
Give thanks . . .

4 When you click your fingers
and you stamp your feet,
when you clap your hands
and you slap your knees,
Give thanks . . .
Give thanks to the Lord. Amen.

346 © 1992 Gillian E Hutchinson

1 **God has made me, and He knows me,**
He will listen to my prayer.
Understanding, ever-loving,
He's the God who's always there.
Even though He made the world, He
knows my name and cares for me.
He will hear me when I call Him;
in His heart I'll always be.

2 Help me, Lord, to understand
that I'm a child who's loved by You.
You'll protect me, and be with me
in the things I have to do.
Thank You, Lord, that I can trust You,
thank You for the love You bring.
Thank You that You'll never leave me;
Father God, Your praise I sing.

347
Fred Pratt Green
© 1973 Stainer & Bell Ltd

1 **God in His love for us lent us this planet,**
gave it a purpose in time and in space:
small as a spark from the fire of creation,
cradle of life and the home of our race.

2 Thanks be to God for its bounty and beauty,
life that sustains us in body and mind:
plenty for all, if we learn how to share it,
riches undreamed of to fathom and find.

3 Long have the wars of man
ruined its harvest;
long has earth bowed to the terror of force;
long have we wasted what others
have need of,
poisoned the fountain of life at its source.

4 Earth is the Lord's: it is ours to enjoy it;
ours, as His stewards, to farm and defend.
From its pollution, misuse and destruction,
good Lord deliver us, world without end!

348
Anon
Copyright control

God loves you, and I love you,
and that's the way it should be.
God loves you, and I love you,
and that's the way it should be.

1 You can be happy, and I can be happy,
and that's the way it should be.
You can be happy, and I can be happy,
and that's the way it should be.
God loves you . . .

2 You can be very sad, I can be very sad;
and that's the way it can be.
You can be very sad, I can be very sad;
and that's the way it can be.
God loves you . . .

3 We can love others like sisters and brothers,
and that's the way it should be.
We can love others like sisters and brothers,
and that's the way it should be.
God loves you . . .

349
Derek Llewellyn
© 1990 Sea Dream Music

1 **God loves you so much,**
God wants you so much,
God wants to tell you so much
that He put it in a book for you.

And it's the Bible,
yes, it's the Bible,
oh, it's the Bible.
Yes, He put it in a letter
so we could know Him better.

2 He wants to know you so much,
He wants to show you so much,
God wants to tell you so much
that He put it in a book for you.
And it's the Bible . . .

3 God loves you so much,
God wants you so much,
God wants to tell you so much
that He put it in a book,
put it in a book for,
put it in a book for you.

350

God of all mercy,
Your forgiveness and compassion
call forth songs from within
that fill our hearts with gladness.

351

God told Joshua to take Jericho.
God told Joshua to take Jericho.
He said, 'Do it My way.'
Joshua said, 'OK.'
So through faith the city walls came down!

1 Marching round the city,
priests are at the front,
blowing on their trumpets,
going round just once.
This they did for six days,
just as God had said;
the priests were making all the noise, the
rest were saying,
God told Joshua . . .

2 God said on day seven,
'Here is what you do:
march around for six times,
then do something new.
When you're on lap seven,
Jericho look out!
All their walls will crumble when you give a
great big SHOUT!!'
God told Joshua . . .

352

1 **God was there before the world**
was made.
God is here, He's with us every day.
God is love and that will never change.
Yesterday, today, forever
He's the same.
Yesterday, today, forever
He's the same.

2 God is good, the Bible tells us so.
God is wise, He knows what we don't know.
God is true, no matter what we do.
Yesterday, today, forever
our life through.
Yesterday, today, forever
our life through.

3 God is like a Father to us all.
God will always listen when we call.
God's the one we worship and adore.
Yesterday, today, forever
He is Lord.
Yesterday, today, forever
He is Lord.

353

1 **God whose love is everywhere**
made our earth and all things fair,
ever keeps them in His care;
    praise the God of love!
He who hung the stars in space
holds the spinning world in place;
    praise the God of love!

2 Come with thankful songs to sing
of the gifts the seasons bring,
summer, winter, autumn, spring;
    praise the God of love!
He who gave us breath and birth
gives us all the fruitful earth;
    praise the God of love!

3 Mark what love the Lord displayed,
all our sins upon Him laid,
by His blood our ransom paid;
    praise the God of love!
Circled by that scarlet band
all the world is in His hand;
    praise the God of love!

4 See the sign of love appear,
flame of glory, bright and clear,
light for all the world is here;
    praise the God of love!
Gloom and darkness, get you gone!
Christ the Light of life has shone;
    praise the God of love!

354
Ian White
© Little Misty Music Ltd

Going up to Jerusalem,
going up to Jerusalem,
going up to Jerusalem, (Jesus going up),
going up to Jerusalem, (Jesus going up).
Going up to Jerusalem,
going up to Jerusalem,
going up to Jerusalem, (Jesus going up),
going up to Jerusalem.

1 Hosanna, hosanna,
we lay our branches down.
Hosanna, hosanna,
the King is coming to our town.
Hosanna, hosanna today.

2 He's the Saviour, He's the Saviour,
we lay our branches down.
He's the Saviour, He's the Saviour,
the King is coming to our town.
Hosanna, hosanna today.

355
Paul Crouch and David Mudie
© 1989 Daybreak Music Ltd

1 **Grace is when God gives us**
the things we don't deserve.
Grace is when God gives us
the things we don't deserve.
He does it because He loves us.
He does it because He loves us.
Grace is when God gives us
the things we don't deserve.

2 Mercy is when God gives us
the things we don't deserve.
Mercy is when God gives us
the things we don't deserve.
He does it because He loves us.
He does it because He loves us.
Mercy is when God gives us
the things we don't deserve.

356
Richard Hubbard
© 1989 Kingsway's Thankyou Music

1 **Hang on, stand still,**
stay put, hold tight;
wait for the Spirit of God.
Don't push, don't shove,
don't move, that's right;
just wait for the Spirit of God.
Hang on . . .

For you will receive the power of God.
You will receive the power of God.
You will receive the power of God
when the Holy Spirit is upon you.

2 Let go, launch out,
press on, don't fight;
be filled with the Spirit of God.
Move on, make way,
step out, that's right;
be filled with the Spirit of God.
Let go . . .

For you have received the power of God.
You have received the power of God.
You have received the power of God
now the Holy Spirit lives within you.

357
Mick Gisbey
© 1985 Kingsway's Thankyou Music

1 **Have you got an appetite?**
Do you eat what is right?
Are you feeding on the word of God?
Are you fat or are you thin?
Are you really full within?
Do you find your strength in Him,
    or are you starving?
You and me all should be
    exercising regularly,
standing strong, all day long,
    giving God the glory.
Feeding on the living bread,
    not eating crumbs but loaves instead;
standing stronger, living longer,
    giving God the glory.
You and me all should be
    exercising regularly,
standing strong, all day long,
    giving God the glory.
Feeding on the living bread,
    not eating crumbs but loaves instead;
standing stronger, living longer,
    giving God the glory.

2 If it's milk or meat you need,
   why not have a slap-up feed,
   and stop looking like a weed
      and start to grow?
   Take the full-of-fitness food,
   taste and see that God is good,
   come on, feed on what you should
      and be healthy.
   You and me all should be
      exercising regularly,
   standing strong, all day long,
      giving God the glory.
   Feeding on the living bread,
      not eating crumbs but loaves instead;
   standing stronger, living longer,
      giving God the glory.
   You and me all should be
      exercising regularly,
   standing strong, all day long,
      giving God the glory.
   Feeding on the living bread,
      not eating crumbs but loaves instead;
   standing stronger, living longer,
      giving God the,
   giving God the, giving God the glory.

358

Ian Smale
© 1988 Kingsway's Thankyou Music

Heavenly Father, we would sing out
   Your praise,
You're everything a Father should be.
Made us Your sons and daughters,
made us Your own,
   children of God's family.

1 We older ones say, 'Younger ones,
   we'll love and care for you.'
   We young ones say to older ones,
   'Our love respects you too.'
   We love you.
   Heavenly Father . . .

2 Father, as a family
   we will live forever.
   Your Church is made of all ages
   who love to be together.
   We love you.
   Heavenly Father . . .

359

Denis and Nan Allen
© 1988 Pilot Point Music / CopyCare Ltd

1 **He made the water wet,**
   He made the land stay dry.
   He put twinkle in the stars
   and blue in the sky.
   And when He was sure
   it worked as it should,
   God looked at His world and said,
   'That's good!'
   Good, good, good! He said, 'That's good!'
   Good, good, good! God looked
      at His world and said,
   'That's good!'

2 He put a touch of wag
   in a puppy dog's tail,
   then put a little slow
   in a silly old snail.
   And when He was sure
   it worked as it should,
   God looked at His world and said,
   'That's good!'
   Good, good, good . . .

   That's good, that's good,
   (shouted) that's good!

360

Peter and Hanneke Jacobs
© 1988 Maranatha! Music / CopyCare Ltd

   He gives me strength, yes,
      He gives me strength.
   I can do all things through Christ
      who gives me strength.
   Yes, He gives me strength,
      He gives me strength.
   I can do all things through Christ
      who gives me strength.

361

Refrain: F Whitfield
Copyright control

QUESTION **Hey, you, (name) do you love**
        Jesus?
ANSWER oh, yes, I love Jesus.
QUESTION Are you sure you love Jesus?
ANSWER Yes, I'm sure I love Jesus.
QUESTION Tell me, why do you love Jesus?
ANSWER This is why I love Jesus,
ALL because He first loved me.
      Yes, I love Him,
        this is why I love Him.

Oh, how I love Jesus.
Oh, how I love Jesus.
Oh, how I love Jesus,
because He first loved me.
Yes, I love Him,
this is why I love Him.

362 Richard K Avery and Donald S Marsh
© 1967 Hope Publishing / CopyCare Ltd

Hey! Hey! Anybody listening?
Hey! Hey! Anybody there?
Hey! Hey! Anybody listening?
Anybody care?

1 We've got good news, good news,
    good news, good news:
Christ the Lord will soon be found here!
Good news, good news,
    good news, good news:
let's help spread the news around here!
If I had a drum I'd drum it,
a mandolin I'd strum it,
a humming-bird hum I'd hum it,
everywhere, everywhere,
    everywhere, everywhere.
Hey! Hey! . . .

2 People come on, come on,
    come on, come on:
let's sing out for Mary's Son here!
Come on, come on, come on, come on:
He'll bring joy for everyone here!
If I had a harp I'd twang it,
a tambourine I'd bang it,
a fireman's bell I'd clang it,
everywhere, everywhere,
    everywhere, everywhere.
Hey! Hey! . . .

3 Come on, sing out, sing out,
    sing out, sing out!
Tell the world about His birth now!
Sing out, sing out, sing out, sing out
loud and clear to all the earth now!
If I had a chime I'd ring it,
a finger cymbal ching it,
we've got this song let's sing it,
everywhere, everywhere,
    everywhere, everywhere.
Hey! Hey! . . .

363 © 1989 Andy Silver

1 **His name was Saul of Tarsus,**
a clever Pharisee;
he studied Greek and Latin
and he spoke them fluently.
The only thing he wanted
was to wipe out those who said,
'We are followers of Jesus
and His truth we want to spread!'
    Saul, Saul, Saul, Saul,
        you're persecuting Me;
    the Christians that you're killing
        are true followers of Me.
    Saul, Saul, Saul, Saul,
        you really need to see
    I came to bring forgiveness and
        to set all people free.

2 Determined to pursue them
on his way he quickly strode,
heading for Damascus
along the well-worn road.
The followers of Jesus
he wanted locked away,
but little did he know
that God would speak to him that day.
    Saul, Saul . . .

3 When God had finished speaking
Saul stood and tried to find
the men who had been with him,
but the light had made him blind.
They led him to a little house,
he stayed for just three days.
When he realised what had happened
he was simply quite amazed.
    Saul, Saul . . .

4 This brought about a change in Saul,
he'd never be the same;
not only had his life been changed
he'd got a different name.
The Lord had given to Paul the task
to go to everyone,
and tell them that the way to God
is only through His Son.
    Saul, Saul . . .

364 Iain Craig
© 1992 Daybreak Music

His ways are not our ways
but His ways are the best.
If we follow Jesus
we know that we'll be blessed.
If we trust Him He will help us,
listen when we pray.
His ways are not our ways
but His ways are the best.

1 When I call He listens, when I fall He's near.
He has promised He will help me,
I will never fear.
His ways . . .

2 If I ever wander, if I turn from Him,
He has promised He will help me,
I will never fear.
His ways . . .

3 He will always love me, He will always care.
He has promised He will help me,
I will never fear.
His ways . . .

365 Carl Tuttle
© 1985 Mercy / Vineyard Publishing / CopyCare Ltd

1 **Hosanna, hosanna,**
 hosanna in the highest;
hosanna, hosanna, hosanna in the highest.
Lord, we lift up Your name,
with hearts full of praise.
Be exalted, O Lord my God –
hosanna, in the highest.

2 Glory, glory, glory to the King of kings;
glory, glory, glory to the King of kings.
Lord, we lift up Your name,
with hearts full of praise.
Be exalted, O Lord my God –
glory to the King of kings.

366 © 1992 Greg Leavers

I am like a house with two windows
 and a door,
but underneath I have two legs
 that reach down to the floor;
two ears to hear what's happening
 and a thatched roof up above,
but right inside God's given me a heart
 that's full of love.
So jump up and turn around
and thank the Lord with joyful sound.
So jump up and turn around
and thank the Lord, and now sit down!

367 Richard K Avery and Donald S Marsh
© 1972 Hope Publishing / CopyCare Ltd

I am the Church! –
 (With your thumb, point to yourself)
You are the Church! –
 (Point to your partner)
We are the Church together! –
 (Shake hands)
All who follow Jesus, –
 (Reach out with both hands)
all around the world, –
 (Circle arms over head)
yes, we're the Church together. –
 (Link arms)

1 The Church is not a building,
 the Church is not a steeple.
The Church is not a resting-place,
 the Church is a people!
I am the Church . . .

2 We're many kinds of people
 with many kinds of faces:
all colours and all ages, too,
 from all times and places.
I am the Church . . .

3 Sometimes the Church is marching,
 sometimes it's bravely burning,
sometimes it's riding, sometimes hiding.
 Always it's learning!
I am the Church . . .

4 And when the people gather there's singing
 and there's praying,
there's laughing and there's crying
 sometimes, all of it saying:
I am the Church . . .

5 At Pentecost some people received
the Holy Spirit
and told the good news through the world
to all who would hear it.
I am the Church . . .

6 I count if I am ninety, or nine, or just a baby;
there's one thing I am sure about
and I don't mean maybe:
I am the Church . . .

368 Peter and Hanneke Jacobs
© 1988 Maranatha! Music / CopyCare Ltd

I am the resurrection and the life.
I am the resurrection and the life.
He that believes in Me though he may die
yet shall he live again.
And whoever lives and believes in Me,
and whoever lives and believes in Me,
the Bible says in John eleven
twenty-five and twenty-six
that we shall never die.

369 Kelly Willard
© 1978 Maranatha! Music / CopyCare Ltd

I cast all my cares upon You.
I lay all of my burdens down at Your feet.
And any time that I don't know what to do,
I will cast all my cares upon You.

I cast all my cares upon You.
I lay all of my burdens down at Your feet.
And any time that I don't know what to do,
I will cast all of my cares upon You.
I will cast all my cares upon You.

370 Susan Sayers
© 1986 Kevin Mayhew Ltd, licence no. 191180

**I have a friend who is deeper
than the ocean;**
I have a friend who is wider than the sky.
I have a friend who always understands me,
whether I'm happy, or ready to cry.

If I am lost He will search until He finds me;
if I am scared He will help me to be brave.
All I've to do is to turn to Him and ask Him.
I know He'll keep the promise He gave:

3 'Don't be afraid,' said Jesus, 'I am with you.'
'Don't be afraid,' said Jesus, 'I am here.
Now and forever, anywhere you travel,
I shall be with you, I'll always be near.'

371 © 1990 Greg Leavers

I look out through the doorway,
who's that I see before me?
My young son coming home.
I must run to meet him,
hug him when I greet him,
and say, 'Son, welcome home.'
We will have a party
and I can't wait to start.
He must have the very finest food,
the best robe, ring and sandals.
He was lost, but now is found.
Welcome home, son, welcome home.

372 Paul Crouch and David Mudie
© 1989 Daybreak Music Ltd

I love You, Lord Jesus,
the King of all things.
You love me, Lord Jesus,
Your love never ends.
To You I am special,
Your promises are true.
You love me, Lord Jesus,
and Lord, I love You.

373 Anon
Copyright control

I am a sheep, baa, baa,
and I like to be well fed;
but like a sheep, baa, baa,
I'm a little stupid in the head.
I go astray most every day.
Oh, what a trouble I must be!
I'm glad I've got the good shepherd
(spoken)
looking after me, ha, ha, ha, ha, baa, baa.

374 Doug Holck
© 1981 Pilot Point Music / CopyCare Ltd

1 **I want to love You, Lord;**
I want to serve You, Lord;
I want to please You, Lord;
this is my prayer.

2 I want to love You, Lord;
   I want to serve You, Lord;
   I want to please You, Lord;
   this is my prayer.

375

1 **I want to tell you (I want to tell you)**
   my eyes are blue (my eyes are blue),
   I want to show you (I want to show you)
   what I can do (*clap! clap!*)
        (what I can do) (*clap! clap!*).
   There's no-one, not one,
     in the world like me.
   I'm so very, very, very, very special,
     you see.
   There's no-one, not one,
     in the world like me,
   for God made me just the way He wanted
     me to be.

2 There are so many (there are so many)
   things I can do (things I can do).
   I don't feel useless (I don't feel useless),
   these words are true (these words are true).
   There's no-one . . .

3 Jesus is special (Jesus is special),
   I'm special too (I'm special too).
   He says He loves me (He says He loves me)
   and He loves you (and He loves you).
   There's no-one . . .

376

I will wave my hands in praise
   and adoration;
I will wave my hands in praise and adoration;
I will wave my hands in praise and adoration,
praise and adoration to the living God.
For He's given me hands
     that just love clapping –
one, two, one, two, three –
and He's given me a voice
     that just loves shouting, 'Hallelujah!'
He's given me feet that just love dancing –
one, two, one, two, three –
and He's put me in a being
     that has no trouble seeing
     that whatever I am feeling
     He is worthy to be praised.

377

I'm a footstep follower
for Jesus leads the way.
He knows the life that's best for me:
a plan for every day.
As I walk and talk with Him,
He'll never let me stray.
I'm a footstep follower
for Jesus leads the way.

378

I'm going to hide God's word
   inside my heart
and learn each verse from memory.
I'm going to hide God's word
   inside my heart
until His word is part of me.

God's word will help me each and every day
to know what is right from what is wrong.
The more that I read it,
   the more I learn of Him,
and His word will make me strong.

That's why I'm going to hide God's word
   inside my heart
and learn each verse from memory.
I'm going to hide God's word
   inside my heart
until His word is part of me,
until His word is part of me.

379

I'm going to say my prayers,
read my Bible every morning;
going to get some fellowship,
witness every day.
I'm going to say my prayers,
read my Bible every morning;
going to get some fellowship,
witness every day.

1 I am going to pray every morning,
   I am going to pray every day.
   I am going to pray every morning,
   I am going to pray every day.
   I'm going to say . . .

2 I am going to read my Bible every morning,
   I am going to read my Bible every day.
   I am going to read my Bible every morning,
   I am going to read my Bible every day.
      I'm going to say . . .

3 I am going to fellowship every morning,
   I am going to fellowship every day.
   I am going to fellowship every morning,
   I am going to fellowship every day.
      I'm going to say . . .

4 I am going to witness every morning,
   I am going to witness every day.
   I am going to witness every morning,
   I am going to witness every day.
      I'm going to say . . .

381

1 **I'm going to take (*clap clap*)
      a step of faith,**
   I'm going to put my trust in the Lord.
   He has the power to carry me through.
   If I listen carefully, He'll tell me what to do.
   I'm going to take (*clap clap*) a step of faith,
   and put my trust in the Lord.

2 I'm going to take (*clap clap*) a step of faith,
   I'm going to put my trust in the Lord.
   He made a promise He loves me so,
   wherever He might lead me,
      He'll never let me go.
   I'm going to take (*clap clap*) a step of faith,
   and put my trust in the Lord.

380 Ernie and Debbie Rettino

**I'm going to stand up,
   I'm going to stand up,**
I'm going to stand up, I'm going to stand up.

*I'm going to stand up,
   stand up and live for Jesus.*
Oo I, I'm going to stand up,
   stand up and live for Him.
I'm going to give up,
   give up my life for Jesus.
Oo I, I'm going to give up,
   give up my life for Him.

Lord, we will live our lives for You,
serve You faithfully, like You want us to.
Lord, You give us the power to live for You,
live for You.

I'm going to stand up . . .

Let's take a stand for Jesus,
let's live our lives for Jesus.
Let's give it all for Jesus.
Stand up for Jesus! Stand up for Jesus!
Stand up, stand up, stand up,
   stand up, stand up!

I'm going to stand up . . .

I'm going to stand up, I'm going to stand up,
I'm going to stand up, I'm going to stand up.
Stand up!

382

I'm going to set my heart
on the precious word of God;
I'm going to feed my heart
on His many promises.
His word helps me in trouble,
it teaches me to praise.
I don't want to live with a hungry heart;
I'm going to feed on the word of God.

383

1 **I've come to a time when I must change,**
   a time when I have to choose,
   to order my own life, or follow Christ,
   and gain what I cannot lose.
      *My Lord, I come,
      I'm giving my life to You.
      Fill me with Your Spirit,
      and make over my heart anew.*

2 The ways of the past, I leave, I leave,
   my life in His hands I place.
   His strength will uphold me
      through anything,
   sufficient for me His grace.
      My Lord . . .

3 The wrong that I've done, I now confess,
   I know that He will forgive.
   His love is far greater than all my sin,
   He'll teach me the way to live.
      My Lord . . .

4 From love of myself, I turn, I turn,
    to serving the King of kings.
    My life will be filled with the love of Christ,
    whatever the future brings.
    My Lord . . .

5 I've come to a time when I must change,
    a time when I have to choose,
    to order my own life, or follow Christ,
    and gain what I cannot lose.

384 Terrye Coelho
© 1973 Maranatha! Music / CopyCare Ltd

If any man come after Me,
    let him deny himself,
pick up his cross and follow Me
into life eternally.
Deny yourself, pick up your cross,
and follow Jesus.
He is the way, truth, and life.

Optional 2nd part

Alleluia! Praise the Lord,
    worship Him in one accord.
Alleluia! He is King,
    Master, Lord of everything.
Jesus Christ, Lord of all,
    loving great and small;
He is the way, truth, and life.

385 © 1992 Gillian E Hutchinson

1 **If it pleases the King,**
    I want to live my life for Him.
    If it offers Him praise,
    I will follow His ways.
    Sinful I may be,
    but He will welcome me.
    My life to Him I'll bring,
    if it pleases the King.

2 If it pleases the King,
    I want to give my love to Him.
    If it honours the Lord,
    I will trust in His word.
    I need never fear,
    for He'll be ever near.
    My love to Him I'll sing,
    if it pleases the King.

386 Sam Horner
© 1991 Daybreak Music Ltd

1 **If Jesus is de vine,**
        we must be de branches.
    If Jesus is de vine, we must be de branches.
    If Jesus is de vine, we must be de branches,
    and bear fruit in the kingdom of God.

2 If Jesus is de rock,
        we should be a little boulder.
    If Jesus is de rock,
        we should be a little boulder.
    If Jesus is de rock,
        we should be a little boulder,
    to bear fruit in the kingdom of God.

3 If Jesus is de bread,
        is your name on the roll now?
    If Jesus is de bread,
        is your name on the roll now?
    If Jesus is de bread,
        is your name on the roll now?
    Let's bear fruit in the kingdom of God.

387 © 1991 Andy Hughes

If you love Me you will
    obey My commandments.
If you love Me you will do what I say;
and if you love Me then every day
    you will seek Me
saying, 'Lord, what shall I do today?'

1 Just like Joshua
    standing at the Jordan's side;
    obeyed the Lord and when he started
        to cross
    the waters opened wide.
    If you love Me . . .

2 As the disciples
    obeyed and brought Him fish and bread.
    So Jesus blessed it and they handed
        it round
    and five thousand men were fed.
    If you love Me . . .

388 Derek Llewellyn
© 1989 Sea Dream Music

1 **If you climb (*stamp stamp*)**
        to the top of a mountain,
    if you swim (*splish splish*) in the ocean blue,
    if you're lost (*sniff sniff*) in the deepest forest
    Jesus will always find you.

If you fall (*scream*) into the darkest cave,
if you fly (*zoom*) right up into the air,
if you run (*run on the spot*)
    all around the world,
Jesus will always be there.

So if you're feeling lonely,
if you're feeling sad,
Jesus will always be close to you,
so you can always feel glad.

If you climb (*stamp stamp*)
    to the top of a mountain,
if you swim (*splish splish*) in the ocean blue,
if you're lost (*sniff sniff*) in the deepest forest,
Jesus will always find you.

89 Michael Ryan
© 1975 Maranatha! Music / CopyCare Ltd

If you want to be great in God's kingdom,
learn to be the servant of all.
If you want to be great in God's kingdom,
learn to be the servant of all.
Learn to be the servant of all,
learn to be the servant of all.
If you want to be great in God's kingdom,
learn to be the servant of all.

90 © Angela Reith

If your empty tum is rumbling
you don't leave your baked beans
        (*munch munch*).
If it's lightning and it's thundering
you don't stand beneath the trees.
And if you climb a high steep hill
you don't refuse a Coke (*pshhh*).
And if your best friend's feeling ill
you don't treat it like a joke (*ha ha*).
You don't run across the high street
if you want to grow old.
You don't look down at your feet
if you want to score a goal (*clap clap*).
So don't forget to pray
if you want to follow God today.
You don't put your Bible out of sight
if you want to do what's right.
You don't put your Bible out of sight
if you want to do what's right.

391 Ian White
© Little Misty Music Ltd

**In everything that I do,
    show me what Jesus would do.**
In everything that I do,
    show me what Jesus would do.
I will not be afraid, for I can always pray,
show me what Jesus would do.

392 Alan J Price
© 1990 Daybreak Music Ltd

*I'm going to shine, shine, shine,
a light in the world I'll be;
I want to shine, shine, shine,
let people see Jesus in me!*

1 I want to glorify the Father
   by the things I do;
   be the person God has made me,
   letting His love flow through!
       I'm going to . . .

2 And when it's hard and it's not so easy
   to know and do what's right;
   I'll trust the Holy Spirit in me,
   to help me win each fight!
       I'm going to . . .

3 Even if I fail Him often
   and my light is dim;
   He has promised to forgive me,
   I can come back to Him!
       I'm going to . . .

393 Marjorie Allen Anderson
© 1947 Scripture Press Publications Inc

1 **In the morning when I rise,**
   when I open up my eyes,
   rain or shine or cold and ice,
   God is near, God is near.

2 When I help and when I play,
   He is there to show the way,
   close behind me all the day,
   God is near, God is near.

3 Then when I turn off the light,
   when I go to sleep at night,
   I am always in His sight,
   God is near, God is near.

394
Harry D Clarke
© 1924 Hope Publishing / CopyCare Ltd

1 **Into my heart, into my heart,**
come into my heart, Lord Jesus.
Come in today, come in to stay;
come into my heart, Lord Jesus.

2 Rule in my heart, rule in my heart,
O King of my heart, Lord Jesus.
Make this Your throne, rule there alone;
O King of my heart, Lord Jesus.

395
Ian White
© Little Misty Music Ltd

It takes an almighty hand,
to make your harvest grow.
It takes an almighty hand,
however you may sow.
It takes an almighty hand,
the world around me shows.
It takes the almighty hand of God.

1 It takes His hand to grow your garden,
all from a secret in a seed;
part of a plan He spoke and started,
and said is 'very good indeed!'
It takes . . .

2 It takes His hand to turn the seasons,
to give the sun and snow their hour;
and in this plan we learn His reason,
His nature and eternal power.
It takes . . .

3 It took His hands to carry sorrow,
for every sin that we have done;
and on a cross He bought tomorrow,
a world of good, like He'd begun.
It takes . . .

4 And in His hands there is perfection,
that in this land we only taste;
for now we see a poor reflection,
then we shall see Him face to face.
It takes . . .

396
Joy Webb
© Salvationist Publishing & Supplies Ltd /
CopyCare Ltd

1 **It was on a starry night**
when the hills were bright,
earth lay sleeping, sleeping calm and still;
then in a cattle shed, in a manger bed
a boy was born, King of all the world.

And all the angels sang for Him,
the bells of heaven rang for Him;
for a boy was born, King of all the world.
And all the angels sang for Him,
the bells of heaven rang for Him;
for a boy was born, King of all the world.

2 Soon the shepherds came that way,
where the baby lay,
and were kneeling, kneeling by His side.
And their hearts believed again,
for the peace of men;
for a boy was born, King of all the world.
And all the angels . . .

On a starry night, on a starry night.

397
© 1989 Andy Silver

1 **It was Jesus who taught His disciples,**
it was Jesus who called them by name.
Then one night on the lake came the wind
and the rain,
and the waves splashed right over the boat.
Splish, splash, pitter pitter pat,
down came the storm with a bang
and a crash.
Splish, splash, pitter pitter pat,
down came the storm with a bang
and a crash.

2 It was Jesus asleep in the trawler,
it was Jesus who woke to their cries.
'Don't you care that we drown,
we're afraid we'll go down!'
and the waves splashed right over the boat.
Splish splash . . .

3 It was Jesus who stood to attention,
it was Jesus who spoke to the waves.
'You, be quiet, do no harm';
right away there was calm.
'Who's this man?' asked the men in the boat.
Splish splash . . .

398
© 1991 Greg Leavers

It's a song of praise,
it's a song of thankfulness;
it's a song of joy,
for every girl and boy.

1 God gave me my hands,
   God gave me my voice;
   God gave me a thankful heart,
   so now I can rejoice.
   It's a song of praise . . .

2 God gave me my feet,
   God gave me my arms;
   the life and love He gives to me
   makes me want to dance.
   It's a song of praise . . .

399 Alan J Price

It's an adventure following Jesus,
it's an adventure learning of Him.
It's an adventure living for Jesus,
it's an adventure following Him.
Let's go where He leads us,
turn away from wrong;
for we know we can trust Him
to help us as we go along.

It's an adventure following Jesus,
it's an adventure learning of Him.
It's an adventure living for Jesus,
it's an adventure following Him.

400 Paul Crouch and David Mudie

It's easy to be a believer,
because it's plain as plain can be
that Jesus came from God and went
to die at Calvary.
But three days later He rose up
and was seen by at least
      five hundred people,
and then went back to heaven
to sit at God's right hand.

401

It's not very nice saying,
   'Na na na na na na';
it's not very good saying, 'It's not fair.'
It's not very kind to fight
      your sister or your brother,
or to sneer at others saying, 'I don't care.'

God doesn't like these things –
He tells us in the Bible they're called sins;
God doesn't like these things.
We do it (*Uh huh*), we know it (*That's right*),
and we need help to stop it.

402 Basil Bridge

1 **It's rounded like an orange,**
   this earth on which we stand;
   and we praise the God who holds it
   in the hollow of His hand.
   So Father, we would thank You
      for all that You have done,
   and for all that You have given us
      through the coming of Your Son.

2 A candle, burning brightly,
   can cheer the darkest night
   and these candles tell how Jesus
   came to bring a dark world light.
   So Father . . .

3 The ribbon round the orange
   reminds us of the cost;
   how the shepherd, strong and gentle,
   gave His life to save the lost.
   So Father . . .

4 Four seasons with their harvest
   supply the food we need,
   and the Spirit gives a harvest
   that can make us rich indeed.
   So Father . . .

5 We come with our Christingles
   to tell of Jesus' birth
   and we praise the God who blessed us
   by His coming to this earth.
   So Father . . .

403 Bacon Boyd

1 **It's the little things that show**
   our love for Jesus.
   It's the little things that show
      our love for Him.
   It's in little things that we can truly serve Him.
   It's with little things that we begin.

Give a little more love
and a little more hope
to others as you serve Him.
Give a little more love
and a little more hope
to others you may meet.
Give a little more love
each day to those around you.
Then a little more love
and a little more faith,
and a little more love and a little more faith
will make you more like Him.

2   It's the little things we do
       each day for others.
    It's the little things that show we really care.
    It's in little things our faith
       becomes much stronger.
    It's with little things that we begin.
    Give a little more love
    and a little more hope
    to others as you serve Him.
    Give a little more love
    and a little more hope
    to others you may meet.
    Give a little more love
    each day to those around you.
    Then a little more love
    and a little more faith,
    and a little more love and a little more faith,
    and a little more love and a little more faith,
    and a little more love and a little more faith
    will make you more like Him.
    I want to be more like Him, more like Him.

404   Ian Smale
       © 1987 Kingsway's Thankyou Music

Jehovah Jireh, God will provide.
Jehovah Rophe, God heals.
Jehovah Makeddesh, God who sanctifies.
Jehovah Nissi, God is my banner.
Jehovah Rohi, God my shepherd.
Jehovah Shalom, God is peace.
Jehovah Tsidkenu, God our righteousness.
Jehovah Shammah, God who is there.

405   © 1989 Andy Silver

1   **Jerusalem man, walking**
       from his homeland,
    when he fell among some robbers,
       poor Jerusalem man.
    They stripped him and they beat him
       with their sticks in their hands;
    poor, poor, poor, poor Jerusalem man.

2   They hastily fled as he fell down and bled,
    but a man who was a preacher saw the
       victim ahead.
    He passed him and ignored him –
       not a word had been said;
    poor, poor, poor, poor Jerusalem man.

3   Along came a man who was very well read,
    now he must have seen the victim
       who by now was half dead.
    He passed him and ignored him
       not a word had been said;
    poor, poor, poor, poor Jerusalem man.

4   The next man to pass, a Samaritan man,
    though he always had been taught
       to hate a true Jewish man,
    he helped him and he took him
       to an inn near his land;
    good, good, good, good Samaritan man.

 Scott Lawrence
       Copyright control

Jesus has promised my shepherd to be,
that's why I love Him so;
and to the children He said, 'Come to Me',
that's why I love Him so.

That's why I love Him, that's why I love Him,
because He first loved me;
when I'm tempted and tried,
       He is close by my side,
that's why I love Him so.

407   © Timothy Dudley-Smith

1   **Jesus, Prince and Saviour,**
    Lord of life who died:
    Christ, the friend of sinners,
    sinners crucified.
    For a lost world's ransom,
    all Himself He gave,
    lay at last death's victim,
    lifeless in the grave.
    Lord of life triumphant,
    risen now to reign!
    King of endless ages,
    Jesus lives again!

2 In His power and Godhead
every victory won,
pain and passion ended,
all His purpose done:
Christ the Lord is risen!
sighs and sorrows past,
death's dark night is over,
morning comes at last!
Lord of life . . .

3 Resurrection morning!
sinners' bondage freed.
Christ the Lord is risen –
He is risen indeed!
Jesus, Prince and Saviour,
Lord of life who died,
Christ the King of glory
now is glorified!
Lord of life . . .

408 Graham Kendrick
© 1986 Kingsway's Thankyou Music

Jesus put this song into our hearts,
Jesus put this song into our hearts;
it's a song of joy no-one can take away.
Jesus put this song into our hearts.

Jesus taught us how to live in harmony,
Jesus taught us how to live in harmony;
different faces, different races,
   He made us one –
Jesus taught us how to live in harmony.

Jesus taught us how to be a family,
Jesus taught us how to be a family;
loving one another
   with the love that He gives –
Jesus taught us how to be a family.

Jesus turned our sorrow into dancing,
Jesus turned our sorrow into dancing;
changed our tears of sadness
   into rivers of joy –
Jesus turned our sorrow into a dance. (*Hey!*)

409 Derek Llewellyn
© 1991 Sea Dream Music

**Jesus, send me the helper,
   send me the helper to help me.**
Jesus, send me the Holy Spirit,
   send the Holy Spirit to me.
Jesus, send me the helper,
   send me the helper to help me.
Jesus, send me the Holy Spirit,
   send the Holy Spirit to me.

He gives us love to keep on loving.
He makes us brave to do what is right.
He gives us faith to keep on going.
He gives us power to keep us
   shining so bright.

Jesus, send me the helper,
   send me the helper to help me.
Jesus, send me the Holy Spirit,
   send the Holy Spirit to me.

410 Otis Skillings
© 1984 Lillenas Publishing Co / CopyCare Ltd

1 **Jesus, I love You, love You, love You.**
Jesus, I love You; Jesus, my Lord.

2 Jesus, I serve You, serve You, serve You.
Jesus, I serve You; Jesus, my Lord.

3 Jesus, I praise You, praise You, praise You.
Jesus, I praise You; Jesus, my Lord;
Jesus, my Lord.

411 J Watson
© Scripture Union

1 **Jesus was the Son of God,**
He became a man.
He was strong and good and kind,
followed all God's plan,
followed all God's plan.

2 When He was a strong young man
Jesus had to die.
All his friends were very sad,
and they wondered why,
and they wondered why.

3 It's so hard to understand
why this had to be;
but I know it was because
He cared for you and me,
He cared for you and me.

412 © 1990 Greg Leavers

Jesus will never, ever,
no not ever, never, ever change.
He will always, always,
that's for all days,
always be the same.

So as Son of God and
King of kings
He will forever reign.
Yesterday, today, forever,
Jesus is the same.
Yesterday, today, forever,
Jesus is the same.

413

Joseph was sold as a slave,
and later was thrown into prison;
but God helped him be very brave,
because he had done nothing wrong.
For God knows, yes, God knows,
 God knows the truth;
for God knows, yes, God knows,
 God knows the truth.

414

Kids under construction;
maybe the paint is still wet.
Kids under construction;
the Lord might not be finished yet.

1 We're more than just accidents
  without the cause;
 we're more than just bodies and brains.
 God made us on purpose,
  we're part of a plan;
 He cares and He knows us by name. Oh!
  Kids under construction . . .

2 Now, mister, I know that I get in your way;
 I'm noisy and just bug you so.
 But there's lots of questions
  I just have to ask
 if I'm ever going to know. Oh!
  Kids under construction . . .

3 Dear Jesus, please make us more
  patient and kind;
 and help us to be more like You.
 And make room for all other children
  of Yours,
 for they are still growing up, too. Oh!
  Kids under construction . . .

415

1 **Large creatures, small creatures,**
 short and tall creatures,
 come now and praise the Lord.
 Young creatures, old creatures,
 hot and cold creatures,
 come now and praise the Lord.
  Sing praise to the Father,
  sing praise to the Son,
  sing praise to the Spirit
  who makes all creatures one.
  Sing praise for the goodness
  of what the Lord has done.
  Let all creatures praise the Lord.

2 Low creatures, high creatures,
 flying in the sky creatures,
 come now and praise the Lord.
 White creatures, brown creatures,
 all the world around creatures,
 come now and praise the Lord.
  Sing praise . . .

3 Day creatures, night creatures,
 left and right creatures,
 come now and praise the Lord.
 Near creatures, far creatures,
 anywhere you are creatures,
 come now and praise the Lord.
  Sing praise . . .

416

Let's go and tell our friends
 that Jesus cares;
let's go and tell our friends that Jesus cares
We've got to go out and tell how Jesus died
 for them;
to tell them how He loves them;
 (*that's right!*)
to tell them He'll forgive them; (*that's true!*)
to tell them He'll be with them; (*Amen!*)
to tell them that He wants to be their friend.

417

Let's praise God together,
let us clap and praise the Lord;
for He loves to hear us –
He is King for evermore.

Jesus, holy is Your name;
high above all others,
power and glory belong to You.
Let's all dance together,
let us dance and praise the Lord;
for he loves to see us –
He is King for evermore.

Jesus, mighty is Your name;
high above all others,
power and glory belong to You.
Let's praise God together,
let us clap and praise the Lord;
for He loves to hear us –
He is King for evermore.

Let's all dance together,
let us dance and praise the Lord;
for he loves to see us –
He is King for evermore.

18 Anon
Copyright control

Long ago there was born,
in the city of David,
a sweet, holy babe who was Jesus,
our King.
Angels sang at His birth,
'Lullaby, peace on earth.'
Angels sang at His birth,
'Lullaby, peace on earth.'

Jesus came as a child
from His Father in heaven,
and has shown us the way to be
loving and kind.
While the stars sang above,
'Lullaby, God is love.'
While the stars sang above,
'Lullaby, God is love.'

19 © 1989 Andy Silver

Long, long ago before our time began
everything was out of shape
and nothing filled the land.
God, who saw the emptiness,
made a plan to clear the mess,
God spoke and it was done.

Day one, came the light and the
day and night;
day two, came the clouds and the
sea and sky;
day three, came the land and the
plants and trees;
day four, came the sun and the
moon and the stars.

2 God took a look and He was happy
and was pleased.
Now the world was taking shape
and all because God breathed;
but He thought the sky and sea
needed some activity –
God spoke and it was done.
Day five, came the fish and the birds that fly;
day six, came the beasts and the animals;
and then came the people called
Adam and Eve;
day seven, all was done and
God rested at ease.

3 God was very glad to see the different forms
of life,
but the part most wonderful was Adam
and his wife.
All He wanted them to do was love
and serve Him through and through;
God spoke and it was done.

420 Bev Gammon
© 1989 Kingsway's Thankyou Music

1 **Lord Jesus,**
You are faithful,
always with us,
never leaving us;
Lord Jesus.

2 Lord Jesus,
You are blameless,
You are perfect,
You are sinless;
Lord Jesus.

3 Lord Jesus,
You are so pure,
pure and lovely,
pure and holy;
Lord Jesus.

421

1 **Lord, make me a mountain**
 standing tall for You;
 strong and free and holy, in everything I do.
 Lord, make me a river of water
  pure and sweet.
 Lord, make me the servant
  of everyone I meet.

2 Lord, make me a candle
  shining with Your light;
 steadfastly unflickering,
  standing for the right.
 Lord, make me a fire burning strong for You.
 Lord, make me be humble in everything I do.

3 Lord, make me a mountain,
  strong and tall for You;
 Lord, make me a fountain
  of water clear and new.
 Lord, make me a shepherd
  that I may feed Your sheep;
 Lord, make me the servant
  of everyone I meet.

422

Lord, we've come to worship You;
Lord, we've come to praise.
Lord, we've come to worship You
in oh, so many ways.
Some of us shout and some of us sing,
and some of us whisper the praise we bring;
but Lord, we all are gathering
to give to You our praise.

423

1 **Lord, You are brilliant,**
  champion of champions;
 to You our thanks and praise we bring.
 You made all the world,
  no-one's as great as You;
 You know everything and all
  Your words are true.
 Lord, You are brilliant,
  champion of champions;
 so we proclaim You are the King.

2 Lord, You are brilliant,
  champion of champions;
 to You our thanks and praise we bring.
 You see everything, all that we say and do;
 You're incredible, no-one loves us like You.
 Lord, You are brilliant,
  champion of champions;
 so we proclaim You are the King.

424

Lord, You are the Light of the world,
 shine in our hearts.
 Let that light shine across the earth,
 Light of the world, our God.

1 In the warmth of Your love
  we would walk in Your light.
 Lord, You are . . .

2 Midst the sorrow of man may
  Your love fill our hearts.
 Lord, You are . . .

3 Lord, the truth and the life,
  revealing Your way!
 Lord, You are . . .

425

Love, joy, peace,
patience, kindness, goodness, faith,
gentleness, and self-control;
this is the fruit of the Spirit.
Love, joy, peace,
patience, kindness, goodness, faith,
gentleness and self-control;
the fruit of the Spirit of God.

You'll find it in Galatians, chapter five,
verse twenty-two.
And if you're walking close to God,
this fruit will grow in you.

And you'll have love, joy, peace,
patience, kindness, goodness, faith,
gentleness, and self-control;
this is the fruit of the Spirit.
Love, joy, peace,
patience, kindness, goodness, faith,
gentleness and self-control;
the fruit of the Spirit of God,
the fruit of the Spirit of God.

426

1 **M-m-m-m-must I really go and visit him?**
I'd n-not be very good at it, you know.
Surely there's s-someone else
   who's w-w-willing to;
I'm a-f-f-fraid to go!

2 He's been p-p-persecuting Your followers,
some have been k-killed, and some were
   thrown in jail.
Please d-d-don't make me go
   and v-v-visit him;
I'll be sh-sh-sure to fail.

Listen, Ananias, I've chosen this man
to be a witness for Me.
Through him, the good news
   will spread to many nations,
bringing life and liberty.

If I really must, Lord, I'll be o-b-bedient;
I know You'll go with me,
   You'll s-see me through.
Even when the task is hard
   or d-d-dangerous,
help me to t-trust in You.

427

Make way, make way,
for Christ the King in splendour arrives;
fling wide the gates
and welcome Him into your lives.
Make way, make way,
for the King of kings;
make way, make way,
and let His kingdom in!

He comes the broken hearts to heal,
the prisoners to free;
the deaf shall hear, the lame shall dance,
the blind shall see.
Make way . . .

And those who mourn with heavy hearts,
who weep and sigh,
with laughter, joy and royal crown
He'll beautify.
Make way . . .

We call you now to worship Him
as Lord of all;
to have no gods before Him,
their thrones must fall!
Make way . . .

428

1 **Matthew had been sitting in his little hut,**
collecting lots of money from the Jews.
He had a reputation, dealing in deception,
working for the Inland Revenue.
Jesus had been walking on the shore
   that day,
and called out, 'Matthew,
   come and follow Me!'
There was no hesitation,
   he didn't even question,
he left his hut and followed straight away.
Come, let's have a party,
come and meet the Lord who called
   and found me;
bring your friends and neighbours
   to the party.
Come, let's have a P.A.R.T.Y.

2 Jesus heard the whispers
   from the Pharisees,
'See Him eating with these wicked men.'
They didn't stop complaining,
   gossiping and jeering,
thinking they were holy, righteous men.
Jesus spoke directly to the Pharisees:
'What sort of people need a doctor's help?
The healthy do not need him, but people
   sick and ailing;
I've come to call all sinners to repent!'
Come, let's have . . .

429

1 **Maybe you can't draw or sing**
   or be a football star;
but just remember, be yourself,
He made you like you are.
It'll be a big thing when Jesus
   takes control,
even though it seems like something
   very slim.
From a tiny lunch He blessed the bread
   and fed the multitudes;
and He'll use us, too,
   when we give ourselves to Him.

2 You may not have the brightest smile
   or make the highest score;
but if you give Him what you have,
He'll make it something more.
It'll be a big . . .

3 If you love our blessèd Lord
      and want to do your part,
   don't worry if you've nothing else –
      the best gift is your heart.
   It'll be a big . . .

430 Mavis Ford
© 1984 Springtide / Word Music (UK) /
CopyCare Ltd

Mighty in victory, glorious in majesty:
every eye shall see Him when He appears,
coming in the clouds with power and glory.
   Hail to the King!
We must be ready, watching and praying,
serving each other, building His kingdom;
then every knee shall bow, then every
      tongue confess,
   Jesus is Lord!

431 Eugene Greco
© 1989 Integrity's Hosanna! Music /
Kingsway's Thankyou Music

Mighty is our God,
mighty is our King.
Mighty is our Lord,
ruler of everything.
Glory to our God,
glory to our King.
Glory to our Lord,
ruler of everything.

His name is higher,
higher than any other name.
His power is greater,
for He has created *everything.

Mighty is our God . . .

* throw arm up in the air

432 © Peter Lewis

Noah was the only good man,
Noah was the only good man,
Noah was the only good man,
and everyone else was bad.

1 The Lord looked at the world He made
      and He was very sad,
   as almost everyone He saw
      was wicked and was bad.
   So God said He would send a flood
      to wash them all away,
   and He said, 'Noah, build an ark
      to float upon the waves!'
   Noah was . . .

2 So Noah built a wooden ark
      the way God told him to,
   and took his family safe inside
      with animals two by two.
   So God saved Noah from the flood
      and promised then and there
   that He would never send again
      a flood upon the earth.
   Noah was . . .

3 God made a rainbow in the sky
      of yellow, blue and red,
   so no-one ever would forget
      the flood and what He said.
   And when we see the rainbow now
      remember God's own words:
   that He would never send again
      a flood upon the earth.
   Noah was . . .

433 © 1992 Gillian E Hutchinson

1 **Now Saul was rejected
      as king of the land,**
   so God spoke to Samuel,
      'Now hear my command.
   Go straight down to Bethlehem,
      there worship Me;
   anoint one of Jesse's sons as king to be!'

2 Now all Jesse's family
      were handsome and strong,
   and when Samuel asked them,
      they all came along;
   and Samuel was wondering
      as in they all trod,
   which one of the brothers
      was chosen by God.

3 He looked on Eliab, and he was impressed
      with the curls of his hair
         and the breadth of his chest;
   but God said to Samuel,
      'That's not where I start –
   you look on his body, but I see his heart!'

So six more fine offspring
  of Jesse's passed by
but each was rejected by God
  the Most High;
then Samuel asked Jesse,
  'Are those all you've got?'
He answered, 'There's David –
  the babe of the lot!'

Now David, the shepherd,
  the youngest of eight,
was out with the sheep on the hills until late.
He had to be sent for; and when he came in,
the Lord said, 'Rise up and
  anoint him as king!'

You may be dressed smartly,
  your face may be fair,
but God's not concerned with
  your clothes or your hair;
your outward appearance is only a part –
when God looks upon you,
  He looks on your heart.

34 Joanne Pond

O give thanks to the Lord,
all you His people;
O give thanks to the Lord,
  for He is good.
Let us praise, let us thank,
let us celebrate and dance;
O give thanks to the Lord,
  for He is good.

35 Ian Smale

O Lord, You're great, You are fabulous.
We love You more than any words can
  sing, sing, sing.
O Lord, You're great, You are so generous;
You lavish us with gifts
  when we don't deserve a thing.
Allelu, alleluia, praise You, Lord.
Alleluia, praise You, Lord,
  alleluia, praise You, Lord.
Allelu, alleluia, praise You, Lord.
Alleluia, praise You, Lord,
  alleluia, praise You, Lord.

2 O Lord, You're great, You are so powerful;
  You hold the mighty universe in Your hand,
    hand, hand.
  O Lord, You're great, You are so wonderful,
  You've poured out Your love
    on this undeserving land.
  Allelu, alleluia . . .

436 Kurt Kaiser

1 **Oh, how He loves you and me;**
  oh, how He loves you and me.
  He gave His life –
  what more could He give?
    Oh, how He loves you;
    oh, how He loves me;
    oh, how He loves you and me.

2 Jesus to Calvary did go,
  His love for sinners to show.
  What He did there
  brought hope from despair.
    Oh, how He . . .

437

  Oh no! The wine's all gone!
  How can the wedding feast now go on?
  Oh dear! What can be done?
  Just listen to Jesus, Mary's Son.
  Oh yes! We'll do what He says –
  fill the stone jars with water that's fresh.
  Oh my! They're pouring it out!
  What, wine? That's a miracle!
    without a doubt!

438 Angela Flynn

1 **Oh, oh, oh, oh, oh, oh, oh, oh.**
  Oh, oh, oh, oh, oh, oh, oh, oh.

2 Hallelujah, hallelujah.
  Hallelujah, hallelujah.

3 Christ died and rose. He will come again.
  Christ died and rose. He will come again.

4 Praise the Lord.
  Praise the Lord.

439 Sam Horner
© 1992 Daybreak Music Ltd

Oh, yes I am, oh, yes I am,
I am saved and kept secure
in Jesus' hand.
Oh, yes I am, oh, yes I am,
I am saved and kept secure
in Jesus' hand.

1 I'm redeemed, the price was paid by Him;
justified, just as if I'd never sinned;
sanctified, holy, set apart;
and it's all because of Jesus' loving heart.
Oh, yes I am . . .

2 I am saved, from death and sin and hell.
I'm empowered, by the Spirit of God as well.
I'm born again, I've got a brand new start;
and it's all because of Jesus' loving heart.
Oh, yes I am . . .

3 I belong to my Father who's above.
I am kept by His never-ending love.
I will survive the devil's fiery darts;
and it's all because of Jesus' loving heart.
Oh, yes I am . . .

440 Anon
Copyright control

1 **Old man Noah built an ark –**
hammer, hammer, bang, bang, ow!
And that old ark was built of wood –
hammer, hammer, bang, bang, ow!
With a saw, saw, here and a nail, nail, there;
here a nail, there a saw,
everywhere a nail, nail;
Old man Noah built an ark –
hammer, hammer, bang, bang, ow!

2 The ark had a door without a knocker –
hammer, hammer, bang, bang, ow!
Everyone said, 'Noah's off his rocker' –
hammer, hammer, bang, bang, ow!
With a 'ha ha' here, and a 'ho ho' there,
here a 'ha', there a 'ho',
everywhere a 'ha ha';
saw, saw here . . .

3 God shut the door and sent the rain –
pitter patter, pitter patter, splosh!
But all the people cried in vain –
pitter patter, pitter patter, splosh!
With a wail, wail here, and a shout,
    shout there,
here a shout, there a wail,
everywhere a shout, shout;
flush, flush here . . .
'ha ha' here . . .
saw, saw here . . .

4 For forty days they were afloat –
pitter patter, pitter patter, splosh!
But they were safe inside God's boat –
pitter patter, pitter patter, splosh!
So trust God here, believe God there,
here believe, there trust,
everywhere believe God;
wail, wail here . . .
flush, flush here . . .
'ha ha' here . . .
saw, saw here . . .

441 Traditional

1 **On Christmas night all Christians sing**
to hear the news the angels bring:
on Christmas night all Christians sing
to hear the news the angels bring:
news of great joy, news of great mirth,
news of our merciful King's birth.

2 Then why should we on earth be so sad,
since our Redeemer made us glad?
Then why should we on earth be so sad,
since our Redeemer made us glad;
when from our sin He set us free,
all for to gain our liberty?

3 When sin departs before His grace,
then life and health come in its place;
When sin departs before His grace,
then life and health come in its place;
angels and men with joy may sing,
all for to see the new-born King.

4 All out of darkness we have light,
which made the angels sing this night:
all out of darkness we have light,
which made the angels sing this night:
'Glory to God and peace to men,
now and for evermore. Amen.'

142 Anthony Welsh
© 1986 Kevin Mayhew Ltd, licence no. 191180

On the road to Damascus
the Lord appeared as a man was riding by:
his name was Saul.
I saw him fall
at a blinding flash from the sky.
'Saul! Saul! Do not persecute Me!
Saul! Saul! Do not persecute Me!'

On the road to Damascus
the Lord cried out to the man
    who could not see.
I heard Him call,
'Now tell Me, Saul,
just why do you persecute Me?
Saul! Saul! Do not persecute Me!
Saul! Saul! Do not persecute Me!'

On the road to Damascus
the Lord's voice came to the man
    whose eyes were blind.
I heard Him call
'Now hear Me, Saul,
I will change your name and your mind.
Saul! Saul! Do not persecute Me!
Saul! Saul! Do not persecute Me!'

On the road to Damascus
I saw him fall to his knees before the Lord.
I heard Him call,
'Your name is Paul,
you must go out and spread My word!
Paul! Paul! Teach the world of Jesus!
Paul! Paul! Teach the world of Jesus!'

On the road to Damascus
yes, I was there when the Lord's
    great power He showed.
I watched as Paul
received God's call
and then on my back he rode!
'Paul! Paul! Teach the world of Jesus!
Paul! Paul! Teach the world of Jesus!'

143 © 1988 Andy Silver

Once upon a time –
    it was many years ago –
Jesus told a story of a man
    that you should know.
He grew up on a farm and
    he had a hundred sheep;
the sheep would eat and eat
    and eat and eat.

'You're the sheep,' Jesus said,
'far from home, all alone.
I have come, God's own Son,
to find you and to bring you back to Him.'

2 When the sun went down
    he would lead them safely home;
one and two and three and four,
    he'd count them on his own.
Then one night he had a fright –
    he counted ninety-nine;
ninety, ninety, ninety, ninety-nine.
    'You're the sheep . . .

3 Out he went to find where the
    missing sheep had strayed;
searching high and low,
    he was feeling quite dismayed.
Then he thought he heard a noise,
    it sounded like a bleat –
he'd found the silly, sad and sorry sheep.
    'You're the sheep . . .

444 Ian White
© Little Misty Music Ltd

1 **Once there was a house,**
    a busy little house;
and this is all about the busy little house.

2 Jesus Christ had come, teaching everyone;
so everyone had to run
    to the busy little house.

3 Everyone was there,
    you couldn't find a chair;
in fact you had to fight for air,
    in the busy little house.

4 A man who couldn't walk,
    was carried to the spot;
but the place was chock-a-block,
    in the busy little house.

5 Whatever shall we do, whatever shall we do?
We'll never get him through
    into the busy little house.

6 We'll open up the roof,
    we'll open up the roof;
and then we'll put him through
    into the busy little house.

7 Then Jesus turned His eyes,
    and saw to His surprise,
the man coming from the skies
    into the busy little house.

8 Then Jesus turned and said,
   'Get up and take your bed,
   and run along instead!'
   from the busy little house.

447 Anon
Copyright control

**Praise and thanksgiving
let everyone bring,**
unto our Father for every good thing!
All together, joyfully sing!

445 © 1991 Greg Leavers

One and two and three and four,
counting sheep in through the door;
fifty-one and fifty-two –
one is lost, what shall I do?
Ninety-eight and ninety-nine,
I will search until I find.
I will keep on looking just because I care.
There he is, caught in some thorns
   way over there,
he was lost but now is found.
So it's ninety-eight, ninety-nine,
   (*click fingers*) one hundred;
yes, it's ninety-eight, ninety-nine,
   (*click fingers*) one hundred!

446 Ian Smale
© 1982 Kingsway's Thankyou Music

1 **Praise Him, praise Him,**
   bring praises to the Lord our God.
   All God's faithful children
   must learn to praise Him.
   Praise Him, praise Him,
   bring praises to the Lord our God.
   All God's faithful children
   must learn to praise Him.
   *Sing hallelu, hallelu,
   sing hallelujah to our God.
   All God's faithful children
   sing hallelujah God.
   Sing hallelu, hallelu,
   sing hallelujah to our God.
   All God's faithful children
   sing hallelujah God.*

2 Worship Him, worship Him,
   bring worship to the Lord our God.
   All God's faithful children
   must learn to worship Him.
   Worship Him, worship Him,
   bring worship to the Lord our God.
   All God's faithful children
   must learn to worship Him.
   Sing hallelu . . .

448 Paul Crouch and David Mudie
© 1991 Daybreak Music Ltd

*Prayer is like a telephone
for us to talk to Jesus.
Prayer is like a telephone
for us to talk to God.
Prayer is like a telephone
for us to talk to Jesus.
Pick it up and use it every day.*

We can shout out loud,
we can whisper softly,
we can make no noise at all;
but He'll always hear our call.

*. . . . . . is like a telephone
for us to talk to Jesus.
. . . . . . is like a telephone
for us to talk to God.
. . . . . . is like a telephone
for us to talk to Jesus.
Pick it up and use it every day.*

We can . . .

*. . . . . . is like a . . . .
for us to talk to Jesus.
. . . . . . is like a . . . .
for us to talk to God.
. . . . . . is like a . . . .
for us to talk to Jesus.
Pick it up and use it every day.*

We can . . .

*. . . . . . is like a . . . .
for us to talk to . . . . .
. . . . . . is like a . . . .
for us to talk to . . .
. . . . . . is like a . . . .
for us to talk to . . . . .
Pick it up and use it every day.
Pick it up and use it every day.
Pick it up and use it every day.*

449 Ian White
© Little Misty Music Ltd

Roll the stone, roll the stone,
roll the stone away.
Jesus died, but He's alive,
and this is Easter day.

We all like to paint our eggs,
sometimes blue and sometimes red.
First we roll them till they crunch,
then we eat them,
(*spoken*) munch, munch, munch!
Roll the stone . . .

We have chocolate eggs to eat,
and inside there's lots of sweets.
First they open with a crunch,
then we eat them,
(*spoken*) munch, munch, munch!
Roll the stone . . .

450 © 1992 Gillian E Hutchinson

Saul had made himself
    a number of enemies,
who were busy plotting his death.
But his friends had no desire to discover him
suffering from shortage of breath.
To avoid a tragedy,
    they removed him secretly,
demonstrating brotherly love.
From enforced captivity,
    carefully they set him free,
demonstrating brotherly love.

Following the Lord can sometimes
    be difficult
if we try to do it alone.
We all need each other's help and
    encouragement
as we learn to live as He's shown;
serving others joyfully, showing generosity,
demonstrating brotherly love;
living in humility, bearing burdens patiently,
demonstrating brotherly love.

3 All of us have different gifts and abilities,
    which we need to learn how to share.
    We can all take part in building
        the fellowship,
    showing the world we care.
    Always speaking truthfully,
        harbouring no enmity,
    demonstrating brotherly love;
    working for Him faithfully,
        joined in perfect unity,
    demonstrating brotherly love.

451 Ian White
© Little Misty Music Ltd

1 **See the man walking,**
        see the man walking,
    see the man walking on the water.
    BOYS *This is a miracle,*
    GIRLS *His name is Jesus.*
    BOYS *How does He do it?*
    GIRLS *He is the Son of God.*
    BOYS *Can I believe Him?*
    GIRLS *You can believe Him.*
    BOYS *Really believe Him?*
    GIRLS *Really believe Him.*

2 Hear the man talking, hear the man talking,
    hear the man talking words of wisdom.
        This is a miracle . . .

3 See the man healing, see the man healing,
    see the man healing people blind and lame.
        This is a miracle . . .

4 See the man dying, see the man dying,
    see the man dying and come back to life.
        This is a miracle . . .

5 Hear the man promise,
        hear the man promise,
    hear the man promise to be with me.
        This is a miracle . . .

452 © Timothy Dudley-Smith

1 **See, to us a Child is born –**
    glory breaks on Christmas morn!
    Now to us a Son is given –
    praise to God in highest heaven.

2 On His shoulder rule shall rest –
    in Him all the earth be blest!
    Wise and wonderful His name –
    heaven's Lord in human frame!

3 Mighty God, who mercy brings –
Lord of lords and King of kings!
Father of eternal days –
every creature sing His praise!

4 Everlasting Prince of peace –
truth and righteousness increase!
He shall reign from shore to shore –
Christ is King for evermore!

453 © 1992 Steve Kersys

**Shine bright, dazzle, dazzle, shine bright,
dazzle, dazzle.**
The light of Jesus is shining bright;
shine bright, dazzle, dazzle, shine bright,
dazzle, dazzle.
The light of Jesus is shining bright.
His life of love;
His life of light;
shines clear and bright in the darkest night.

454 From Psalm 98
© Timothy Dudley-Smith

1 **Sing a new song to the Lord,**
He to whom wonders belong!
Rejoice in His triumph and tell of His power –
O sing to the Lord a new song!

2 Now to the ends of the earth
see His salvation is shown;
and still He remembers His mercy and truth,
unchanging in love to His own.

3 Sing a new song and rejoice,
publish His praises abroad!
Let voices in chorus, with trumpet and horn,
resound for the joy of the Lord!

4 Join with the hills and the sea
thunders of praise to prolong!
In judgement and justice
He comes to the earth –
O sing to the Lord a new song!

455 Derek Llewellyn
© 1991 Sea Dream Music

1 **Sing praise to God the Father,**
God the Spirit, God the Son.
Sing praise to God who loves us.
Praise Him, everyone!

2 Sing praise to God the Father,
clap your hands and jump for joy.
He made the world around us
and He loves us all.

3 Sing praise to God's Son Jesus,
clap your hands and jump for joy.
Wave your arms and turn around.
He teaches us about the Father
and He loves us all.

4 Sing praise to the Holy Spirit,
clap your hands and jump for joy.
Wave your arms and turn around.
Stamp your feet and shout hooray.
He helps us to live like Jesus
and He loves us all.

5 Sing praise to God the Father,
God the Spirit, God the Son:
Sing praise to God who loves us.
Praise Him everyone!

456 © 1991 Greg Leavers

*Sing and celebrate (sing and celebrate
God gave Jesus (God gave Jesus);
Light for all the world
(Light for all the world);
born at Christmas (born at Christmas time*

1 Jesus, our light,
shines bright,
what delight;
came to reach us,
teach us,
lead us;
Sing and celebrate . . .

2 God so loved us,
gave us
Jesus;
Lord, we thank You,
love You,
serve You;
Sing and celebrate . . .

*Jesus, Light of the world,
God's great gift of love.*

457 © 1991 Greg Leavers

*Sing and celebrate (sing and celebrat
Christ is risen (Christ is risen);
Champion of the world
(Champion of the world);
lives for ever (lives for evermore).*

1 God so loved us,
  gave us
  Jesus;
  died on Calvary,
  set free
  you and me;
  Sing and celebrate . . .

2 Jesus our friend,
  died, then
  rose again;
  Lord, we love You,
  thank You,
  praise You;
  Sing and celebrate . . .

  *Jesus died for the world,
  God's great gift of love.*

3 King Nebuchadnezzar lost his religion
  when the Hebrews wouldn't bow down.
  He lost his cool, fired up the furnace,
  called a holiday in the town.
  When he opened the door
      and threw them in,
  they smiled at the burning coals,
  'cause the God that allowed that fire to burn
  had everything under control.
      He's got everything . . .

4 Daniel was invited to be on the menu
  at the meeting of the lions' club,
  'cause he continued to pray
      three times a day
  to the Lord he had learned to love.
  When they threw him in he began to grin,
  'cause he knew what we all know;
  that the God who made those lions growl
  had everything under control.
      He's got everything . . .

459 Ian Smale
© 1978 Kingsway's Thankyou Music

So we're marching along, singing a song,
we're in the Lord's army.
We're fighting for right as we're learning
    what's wrong,
'cause – we're in the Lord's army.
He's got the victory, so let's really shout,
we're in the Lord's army.
We're in the Lord's (*yeah*),
    we're in the Lord's (*right*),
we're in the Lord's army.
So we're marching along . . .

158 Eddie Smith
© 1978 Pilot Point Music / CopyCare Ltd

**Six hundred years old
    was the preacher Noah**
when the Lord said to build a boat;
said a flood would come
    and cover the earth,
and only Noah would stay afloat.
Though the people laughed
    and called him names,
he stayed right with his job.
When he felt those drops, he knew his God
had everything under control.
    *He's got everything under control,
    He's got everything under control.
    The stars and the planets are in His hand,
    the wind and the rain at His command.
    You and I, we're a part of His plan;
    He's got everything under control.*

Now Jonah had a whale of a problem
when he turned that revival down.
God tracked him down and boxed him in
'cause he wouldn't go to that town.
When He tells you to do
    what He wants you to do,
don't think you can let it roll,
'cause the God who made this universe
has everything under control.
    He's got everything . . .

460 © 1990 Greg Leavers

1 **Sometimes I'm naughty,**
  I know I've been bad;
  I say such unkind things
  and make people sad.
      *Father, I know I've done wrong;
      Lord, please forgive me I pray.
      I want to say,
      I want to say
      that I'm so sorry, Lord.*

2 I'm rude to my family,
  I want my own way.
  I don't show them kindness
  or do what they say.
      Father, I know . . .

3 In love You forgive me,
I'm glad I'm Your child.
Your Spirit lives in me
to change me inside.
*Father, help me today;
help me to please You, I pray.
I want to say,
I want to say
how much I love You, Lord.*

461

1 **Sometimes problems can be BIG,**
sometimes problems can be *small*;
but it doesn't really matter
for whatever the size,
Jesus wants to help us with them all –
so we can tell Him all about it.
Trust His word, don't doubt it.
Don't be afraid;
DON'T BE AFRAID,
just (1, 2, 3, 4) believe.

2 Some days I wake up feeling GLAD,
some days I wake up feeling *sad*;
but it doesn't really matter
for whatever the day
Jesus wants to help us through them all.
He's promised He will never leave us;
He will not forsake us;
don't be dismayed,
DON'T BE AFRAID,
just (1, 2, 3, 4) believe.

Words in Capitals spoken with a loud voice
Words in Italics spoken quietly

462 Sam Horner

1 **Some people laugh, some people sing,**
some people clap; and so they bring
their worship to the King of kings.
What do you do? What do you do?

2 Some people dance, some bring a word,
some people cry before the Lord;
and so they bring their worship to
the King of kings, the King of kings.

3 Some people march and raise their hands
and some are quiet but understand.
There are many ways of worshipping
the King of kings, the King of kings.

463

1 **Sorry, Lord, for all the things**
that I've done wrong; please
make me clean, forgive my sin –
I want to follow You.

2 Thank You, Lord, for dying on
the cross to save me;
fill my heart for my new start –
please come and live in me.

3 I love You, please help me Lord
to follow closely;
from today, in every way
please make me more like You.

464

1 **Spies were sent out to**
view the promised land.
Ten said, 'There are giants there:
we can't do as we planned.'
Joshua and Caleb said,
'We must make a stand.'
The Lord said, 'Follow Me,
I'll place them in your hand.'
*We've got to hear, believe and obey,
whatever the Father might say;
for He is a good God and He only wants
the best for us.*

2 When Joshua saw the size of
Jericho's great wall –
towering high above him,
many metres tall –
though it looked impossible
to take the town at all,
the Lord said, 'Obey Me
and down the walls will fall.'
We've got to . . .

3 So when you're feeling scared or
things are looking blue –
you've a job that seems so
difficult to do –
don't forget His promises
He's made to help you through:
the Lord says, 'Don't be afraid,
I'll always be with you.'
We've got to . . .

465
Ian Smale
© 1984 Kingsway's Thankyou Music

**Spirit of God, please fill me
    now to overflowing.**
Spirit of God, give me the words
    You want me to say.
Spirit of God, release my tongue to
    praise the Holy Son;
Spirit of God, free this spirit of mine.

466
© 1992 Gillian E Hutchinson

*Standing in Your presence, Lord,
we are here to praise Your name.
Standing in Your presence, Lord,
Your great goodness we proclaim.*

You alone are God the Lord,
Master of the earth and sky.
All the stars in heaven worship, and yet,
when we call You Lord, You hear our cry.
    *Standing in Your presence, Lord,
    we will lift our hands to You.
    Standing in Your presence, Lord,
    giving thanks for all You do.*

You have brought us here today,
kept and guided for so long.
There's no need for tears or sadness,
the joy that You give us, Lord,
    will make us strong.
    *Standing in Your presence, Lord,
    listening to Your holy law.
    Standing in Your presence, Lord,
    we will praise You evermore.*

467
© 1989 Andy Silver

**Thank You for the love
    that our mums give to us each day;**
thank You for the help
    and the care that they bring our way.
Lord, we thank You for everything they do,
show us how to help them too.
Show us how to live,
    teaching us to appreciate;
show us how to live
    so that we don't infuriate.
Lord, we ask that in everything they do,
may our mums be blessed by You.

468
Valerie Collison
© 1970 High-Fye Music Ltd

1 **The journey of life may be easy,
        may be hard,**
    there'll be dangers on the way;
    with Christ at my side I'll do battle as I ride
    'gainst the foe that would lead me astray.
        *Will you ride, ride, ride
        with the King of kings,
        will you follow my Leader true;
        will you shout 'Hosanna!'
        to the holy Son of God,
        who died for me and you?*

2 My burden is light and a song is in my heart,
        as I travel on life's way;
    for Christ is my Lord and
        He's given me His word,
    that by my side He'll stay.
        Will you ride . . .

3 When doubts arise and when tears
        are in my eyes,
    when all seems lost to me;
    with Christ as my guide I can smile
        whate'er betide,
    for He my strength will be.
        Will you ride . . .

4 I'll follow my Leader wherever he may go,
        for Jesus is my friend;
    He'll lead me on to the place
        where He has gone,
    when I come to my journey's end.
        Will you ride . . .

469
Paul Kenchington
© 1984 Kevin Mayhew Ltd, licence no. 191180

1 **The Lord is risen today!**
    The Lord is risen today!
    The Lord is risen today!
    The Lord is risen today!
    Alleluia! Alleluia! Alleluia!
    The Lord is risen today!

2 And we will sing His praise,
    and we will sing His praise,
    and we will sing His praise;
    the Lord is risen today!
    Alleluia! Alleluia! Alleluia!
    The Lord is risen today!

3 O, Jesus died for me!
Yes, Jesus died for me!
Yes, Jesus died for me,
but the Lord is risen indeed!
Alleluia! Alleluia! Alleluia!
The Lord is risen today!

All sing 1 in unison, followed by 2 in unison.
One group begins 1 again and as they reach 2,
the other group begins at 1.
The accompaniment is common in both 1 and 2.

 470 Ian Smale
© 1985 Kingsway's Thankyou Music

**The most important thing
for us as Christians**
is not what we eat or drink,
but stirring up goodness, peace and joy
from the Holy Spirit.

3 He died in pain on Calvary,
walk, walk in the light;
to save the lost like you and me,
walk, walk in the light.
Walk in the light . . .

4 We know His death was not the end,
walk, walk in the light;
He gave His Spirit to be our friend,
walk, walk in the light.
Walk in the light . . .

5 By Jesus' life our wounds are healed,
walk, walk in the light;
the Father's kindness is revealed,
walk, walk in the light.
Walk in the light . . .

6 The Spirit lives in you and me,
walk, walk in the light;
His light will shine for all to see,
walk, walk in the light.
Walk in the light . . .

 471 Hilda Rostron
© National Christian Education Council

1 **The shepherds found the stable**
and saw the Baby there;
they quietly knelt beside Him
and said a 'thank you' prayer.

2 The wise men found the Baby
and gave gifts, one, two, three;
today it is His birthday:
My gift is – LOVE from me.

472 Damien Lundy
© Kevin Mayhew Ltd, licence no. 191180

1 **The Spirit lives to set us free,**
walk, walk in the light;
He binds us all in unity,
walk, walk in the light.
*Walk in the light,
walk in the light,
walk in the light,
walk in the light of the Lord.*

2 Jesus promised life to all,
walk, walk in the light;
the dead were wakened by His call,
walk, walk in the light.
Walk in the light . . .

473 Alan J Price
© 1990 Daybreak Music Ltd

**The word of the Lord is
planted in my heart**
and I want to see it grow.
The word of the Lord is planted in my heart
and I want you to know.
I won't let the enemy take it,
or let bad times shake it;
I won't let other things choke it out,
    (*choke choke choke choke*)
'cause I want to let it grow, grow, grow,
'cause I want to let it grow! (*last time*) (*Yeah!*)

474 Mick Gisbey
© 1985 Kingsway's Thankyou Music

The word of God is living and active,
sharper than any double-edged sword.
The word of God is living and active,
sharper than any double-edged sword.

475

There he stood – Goliath –
mighty man in armour bright;
compared to him you'd not say David
    was prepared to fight.
When Goliath saw him,
    he could not believe his eyes:
before him stood a boy he did despise.
'Do you think I am a dog,
    to fight me with a stick?
I'll throw your flesh to animals,
    your bones for birds to pick!'
Shouting murderous curses, he cried out,
    'Prepare to die!'
But David spoke up boldly in reply.
    'Not with spear, not with sword
    but in the name of the Lord;
    in the name of the One you have defied.
    He's victorious in battle,
    He will save us by His power;
    strength and deliverance He'll provide;
    I'm fighting on the Lord almighty's side!'

Moving closer in, Goliath started his attack
but David ran to meet him –
    he did not turn and run back.
With his sling he threw a stone
    which to Goliath sped;
it broke his skull and sank into his head!
The giant had been conquered –
    he fell down upon the floor –
then David chopped his head off
    and Goliath was no more!
All of Israel's army knew
    the mighty deed was done
and in whose name the victory
    had been won.
    'Not with spear . . .

Life is filled with problems
    which may give us cause to fear.
But though they seem like giants,
    just remember God is near.
He will always help us
    when we put our trust in Him.
In the name of Jesus we shall win.
    'Not with spear . . .

476

There is no-one else like you,
there's no-one else like me.
Each of us is special to God,
that's the way it's meant to be.
I'm special, you're special,
we're special, don't you see?
there is no-one else like you,
there's no-one else like me.

Black or white, short or tall,
good or bad, God loves us all.
Loud or quiet, fat or thin,
each of us is special to Him.

There is no-one . . .

477

There once was a man called Daniel
(*good old Daniel*).
And Daniel prayed three times a day
(*good old Daniel*).
But the King's decree said, 'Worship me!'
(*poor old Daniel*).
But Daniel would not bend the knee!
(*good old Daniel*).
So the gates went 'crash' (*crash*),
and the locks went 'click' (*click*),
and the lions began to roar,
and the lions began to roar.
But they couldn't eat Daniel if they tried
(*good old Daniel*),
because the Lord was on his side
(*good old Daniel*).

478

1 **There's a song for all the children**
    that makes the heavens ring,
    a song that even angels
    can never, never sing;
    they praise Him as their maker
    and see Him glorified,
    but we can call Him Saviour
    because for us He died.

2 There's a place for all the children
where Jesus reigns in love,
a place of joy and freedom
that nothing can remove;
a home that is more friendly
than any home we know,
where Jesus makes us welcome
because He loves us so.

3 There's a friend for all the children
to guide us every day,
whose care is always faithful
and never fades away;
there's no-one else so loyal –
His friendship stays the same;
He knows us and He loves us,
and Jesus is His name.

479 Susan Sayers
© 1984 Kevin Mayhew Ltd, licence no. 191180

1 **Think big: an elephant.**
Think bigger: a submarine.
Think bigger: the highest mountain that
anyone has ever seen.
Yet big, big, bigger is God!
And He loves us all.

2 Think old: a vintage car.
Think older: a full-grown tree.
Think older: a million grains of the sand
beside the surging sea.
Yet old, old, older is God!
And He loves us all.

3 Think strong: a tiger's jaw.
Think stronger: a castle wall.
Think stronger: a hurricane that leaves little
standing there at all.
Yet strong, strong, stronger is God!
And He loves us all.

480 Graham Kendrick
© 1988 Make Way Music

1 **This Child secretly comes in the night;**
oh, this Child, hiding a heavenly light;
oh, this Child, coming to us like a stranger;
this heavenly Child.
This Child, heaven come down
now to be with us here;
heavenly love and mercy appear;
softly in awe and wonder come near
to this heavenly Child.

2 This Child, rising on us like the sun;
oh, this Child, given to light everyone;
oh, this Child, guiding our feet
on the pathway
to peace on earth.
This Child, heaven come down . . .

3 This Child, raising the humble and poor;
oh, this Child, making the proud ones to fall
this Child, filling the hungry
with good things;
this heavenly Child.
This Child, heaven come down . . .
This Child, heaven come down . . .

481 Alan J Price
© 1990 Daybreak Music Ltd

This is a catchy songa,
we sing it to the Conga,
we dance and sing
to Christ the King.
Why don't you sing alonga,
while we dance the Conga?
Praise God above for all His love!

1 King David danced before the Lord,
worship filled his heart;
we can dance before Him, too,
this is how we start.
This is a catchy songa . . .

2 Jesus is the greatest friend,
alive for us today,
He said, 'I'm with you till the end,
I'm with you all the way.'
This is a catchy songa . . .

Verses spoken, not sung

482 © 1985 Andy Silver

Wandering like lost sheep,
we were going our own way,
when Jesus the good shepherd
found us, led us home,
laid down His life before us
that we might all be saved.
We now belong to Jesus,
we now belong to Him.
We are His sheep, we are His sheep,
we hear His voice, and follow Him.
We are His sheep, we are His sheep,
we hear His voice, and follow Him.

483

We are soldiers of the King,
of His victory we will sing;
living every hour by the Spirit's power,
marching in the name of Jesus.
Enemies are all around,
as we praise they're losing ground;
trusting in God's word – it's a mighty sword –
forever friendly, faithful followers fighting for
    the King.

484

We need to grow, grow, grow, grow,
grow in the grace of the Saviour.
We need to grow, grow, grow, grow,
grow in the knowledge of Jesus our Lord.
We need to grow, grow, grow, grow,
grow in the grace of the Saviour.
We need to grow, grow, grow, grow,
grow in the knowledge of Jesus our Lord.

1 We'll grow as we pray to Him,
    spend some time each day.
    We'll grow as we worship Him,
    give Him our love and praise!
    We need to grow, grow, grow, grow,
    grow in the grace of the Saviour.
    We need to grow, grow, grow, grow,
    grow in the knowledge of Jesus our Lord.

2 We grow as we read of Him
    and the way for us to live;
    we'll grow as we work for Him,
    as our lives to Him we give.
    We need to grow . . .

3 We grow as we learn and share
    with others that we know;
    these are the things to do
    if we really want to grow.
    We need to grow . . .
    grow in the knowledge of,
    grow in the knowledge of Jesus our Lord.

485

We will praise, we will praise,
    we will praise the Lord;
we will praise the Lord because He is good.
We will praise, we will praise,
    we will praise the Lord,
because His love is everlasting.
We will praise, we will praise,
    we will praise the Lord;
we will praise the Lord because He is good.
We will praise, we will praise,
    we will praise the Lord,
because His love is everlasting.

Bring on the trumpets and harps,
let's hear the cymbals ring;
then in harmony
lift our voices and sing, sing.

We will praise, we will praise,
    we will praise the Lord;
we will praise the Lord because He is good.
We will praise, we will praise,
    we will praise the Lord,
because His love is everlasting.

486

1 **We'll praise Him on the trumpet**
        and we'll praise Him on guitar,
    we'll praise Him with a drum
        and with a harp and a lyre.
    We'll praise Him with our voices
        'cause we want to lift Him higher;
    and all God's people shout, 'Hallelujah!'
    Hallelujah, hallelujah, hallelujah, hallelujah.
    Hallelujah, hallelujah,
        and all God's people shout, 'Hallelujah!'

2 We'll praise Him for His favour
        and we'll praise Him for His deeds;
    we'll praise Him – though the road is rough,
        He's still the one who leads.
    We'll praise Him for provision
        as He cares for all our needs,
    and all God's people shout, 'Hallelujah!'
    Hallelujah, hallelujah . . .

3 We'll praise Him that upon a cross
    the Lamb of God was slain;
we'll praise Him that He conquered death
    and now He lives again.
We'll praise Him – He's the King of kings
    who will forever reign,
and all God's people shout, 'Hallelujah!'
    Hallelujah, hallelujah . . .

4 We'll praise Him that He's making us
    the people we should be;
we'll praise Him that our chains are gone,
    we're now completely free.
We'll praise Him – we don't know defeat,
    we live in victory,
and all God's people shout, 'Hallelujah!'
    Hallelujah, hallelujah . . .

487 Robert C Evans
© 1990 Integrity's Hosanna! Music /
Kingsway's Thankyou Music

We're following Jesus,
just like Matthew, Peter and John.
We're following Jesus,
just like Thaddeus, Philip and Tom.
We're following Jesus,
just like Simon, James and Andrew.
Like them, the Lord is calling me and you.

1 They all loved Him (*I want to love Him*),
they all served Him (*I want to serve Him*).
They all knew Him (*I want to know Him*),
they all followed. (*I want to follow*).
    We're following . . .

2 Jesus taught them (*Teach me, Lord*),
Jesus led them (*Lead me, Lord*),
Jesus fed them (*Feed me, Lord*),
Jesus used them (*Use me, Lord*).
    We're following . . .

488 © Timothy Dudley-Smith

1 **What colours God has made**
in flower and field and tree!
From springing green of leaf and blade
I learn His love for me.

2 The summer's yellow sand,
the blue of sky and sea,
they tell of God their maker's hand,
and all His love for me.

3 The turning autumn leaves,
the fruit so full and free,
the golden glow of harvest sheaves,
declare His love for me.

4 He frames the winter's skies,
His silver stars I see;
He makes the sun in splendour rise,
the God who cares for me.

5 So sing my Father's praise,
the living God is He,
whose colours brighten all our days,
who loves and cares for me.

489 Nancy Harrison
© 1981 Lillenas Publishing Co / CopyCare Ltd

1 **What do you give a God**
    who has everything?
What do you give a God who has it all?
He is the One who flung the
    shining galaxies in space!
He is the One who hung the stars in place!

2 What do you give a God
    who has everything?
What do you give the maker of the earth?
Give Him your life and let Him guide you;
trust Him in all your ways!
Give Him your heart;
    He'll fill it up with praise!
Give Him your heart;
    He'll fill it up with praise!

490 William and Gloria Gaither
© 1975 Kingsway's Thankyou Music

1 **What drives the stars**
    without making a sound?
Why don't they crash
    when they're spinning around?
What holds me up when
    the world's upside down?
I know it's a miracle!
Who tells the ocean
    where to stop on the sand?
What keeps the water
    back from drowning the land?
Who makes the rules I don't understand?
I know it's a miracle!
    It's a miracle just to know
    God is with me wherever I go.
    It's a miracle as big as can be,
    that He can make a miracle of me!

2 Who shows the birds
     how to make a good nest?
   How can the geese fly so far without rest?
   Why do the ducks go south and not west?
   I know it's a miracle!
   What makes a brown seed so tiny and dry
   burst into green and grow up so high?
   And shoot out blossoms of red by and by?
   I know it's a miracle!
     It's a miracle . . .

3 When a spring makes a brook
     and a brook makes a stream,
   the stream makes the river water
     fresh as can be.
   Who puts the salt in when it gets to the sea?
   I know it's a miracle!
   There are thousands of people in cities I see,
   the world must be crowded
     as crowded can be;
   but God knows my name
     and He cares about me.
   I know it's a miracle!

491 Anon
Copyright control

1 **What a mighty God we serve . . .**
   (*4 times*)

2 He created you and me . . .

3 He has all the power to save . . .

4 Let us praise the living God . . .

5 What a mighty God we serve . . .

492 © 1992 Gillian E Hutchinson

1 **What made a difference in the life of Saul,**
   to change him from a sinner to Apostle Paul?
   He met Jesus and suddenly knew
   that all he'd hated turned out to be true.
   Instead of persecuting those
     who followed His name,
   he started in the synagogue His love
     to proclaim.
   Yes, who'd have thought that Saul could be
   transformed into the greatest missionary.

2 On several journeys the apostle was sent,
   and suffered many difficulties as he went.
   Beaten, shipwrecked, imprisoned was he
   but learnt to glory in adversity.
   The churches grew and flourished
     and the Gospel was spread,
   and many found salvation
     through the things that he said.
   Yes, who'd have thought that Saul could be
   transformed into the greatest missionary.

3 He wrote some letters to the churches
     he knew,
   to Ephesus, Colossi and Galatia too.
   To Philippi and Corinth he wrote,
   to Rome and Thessalonica, epistles of note.
   Timothy and Titus and Philemon all heard
   and what he wrote has now become
     a part of God's Word.
   Yes, who'd have thought that Saul could be
   transformed into the greatest missionary.

4 If you've decided that your life must change,
   then give it to the Lord for Him to rearrange.
   He will be your Saviour and friend,
   and on His presence you can depend.
   You may not be a missionary
     or travel around,
   but all of us can witness to the joy
     that we've found.
   Yes, what the Lord could do for Saul,
   He's ready now to do for one and all!

493 © 1991 Greg Leavers

When I'm feeling lonely,
     when I'm feeling blue,
   when I'm feeling so fed up,
     I can always talk to You.
   Lord, You hear me when I pray;
   Lord, You're near me every day.
   Thank You, Lord,
     You always see me through;
   I'll never, ever, find a friend as good as You.
   I'll never, ever, find a friend as good as You.

494 Paul Field and Ralph Chambers
© 1991 Daybreak Music Ltd

When the dark clouds are above you,
   there's no sunshine anywhere;
   when you feel that no-one loves you,
   when you feel that no-one cares;
   talk to the Saviour,
   He knows how you feel.

His love lasts forever,
His love for you is real.
Talk to the Saviour,
no matter what you do.
You've got a friend in Jesus,
He always loves you.

When the dark . . .

495 © 1988 Andy Silver

When we look up to the sky
and we see the sparrows fly,
let's remember that Jesus knows them all.
When we see the lovely trees
and the flowers and the leaves,
let's remember that Jesus made them all.
J.E.S.U.S. C.A.R.E.S.
Jesus cares for all the things He made:
that means you and me,
our friends and family.
Thank You, Jesus, for caring for me.

496 Paul Field and Ralph Chambers
© 1991 Daybreak Music Ltd

When you're feeling good
 put your thumbs up.
When you're feeling bad put them down.
When you're feeling happy
 you can smile all day.
When you're feeling low wear a frown.
But don't just follow your feelings.
Trust in God and His word.
No matter what you feel put your thumbs up,
put your faith in the Lord.

497 © 1991 Joan Robinson

When God breathes His Spirit in my life;
when God breathes His Spirit in my life;
when God breathes His Spirit in my life,
then I will shine, shine for Him.

498 P M Verrall
© Herald Music Service

1 **Would you walk by on the other side**
when someone called for aid?
Would you walk by on the other side,
and would you be afraid?
Cross over the road, my friend;
ask the Lord His strength to lend;
His compassion has no end.
Cross over the road.

2 Would you walk by on the other side
when you saw a loved one stray?
Would you walk by on the other side,
or would you watch and pray?
Cross over the road . . .

3 Would you walk by on the other side
when starving children cried?
Would you walk by on the other side,
and would you not provide?
Cross over the road, my friend,
ask the Lord His strength to lend,
His compassion has no end.
Cross over the road.
Cross over the road,
cross over the road.

499 Ian Smale
© 1987 Kingsway's Thankyou Music

Yet to all who received Him,
to those who believed in His name,
He gave the right to become
 the children of God.
Yet to all who received Him,
to those who believed in His name,
He gave the right to become
 the children of God.

500 © 1991 Greg Leavers

You are holy, so You hate all we do wrong.
You are loving, for our sin
 You gave Your Son.
You are Father, the great protector;
You are mighty, the great Creator;
You are faithful, You are wonderful,
You are King and You are God.

501

1 **You can weigh an elephant's auntie,**
you can weigh a pedigree flea;
but you can't weigh up all the love
that Jesus has for me, me, me,
that Jesus has for me.

2 You can measure the length
    of a wiggly worm,
or the height of a nanny goat's knee;
but you can't measure all the love
that Jesus has for me, me, me,
that Jesus has for me.

3 You can add up two and two, make four,
it's as easy as A, B, C;
but you can't add up all the love
that Jesus has for me, me, me,
that Jesus has for me.

4 You can amaze me by subtraction,
you can even take three from three;
but you can't take away the love
that Jesus has for me, me, me,
that Jesus has for me.

502

**You can't catch a plane
    to take you to heaven.**
Not even a spaceship can get that far.
You can't take a hovercraft
    or helicopter journey
or drive in the fastest racing car.
Only Jesus, only Jesus,
    only Jesus is the way.
Only Jesus, only Jesus,
    only Jesus is the way.

503

You're my maker, You're my music,
You're the Master of my life.
You're my maker, You're my music,
You're the Master of my life.
You're my maker, You're my music,
You're the Master of my life,
and I love You, Jesus my Lord.

Copyright Addresses

Allen, F R, Barton Cottage, Station Road, Blockley, Glos GL56 9DT
Arlott, B M, c/o W S V Kennard, J Kay-Mouat, The Old Presbytery, Alderney, Channel Islands GY9 3TF
Booth, J A P, c/o Paul Booth, 2 Old Coastguard Cottages, Waterside, Bradwell-on-Sea, Essex CM0 7QY
Bosworth & Co Ltd, 14-18 Heddon Street, London W1R 8DP
Brown, Alan, 11 The Quadrant, Wimbledon, London SW20 8SW
Burt, Phil, 5 Gardner Road, Warton, Carnforth, Lancs LA5 9NY
Bush, Annie c/o Mrs A Spiers, 40 Northumberland Terrace, Everton, Liverpool L5 3QG
Cansdale, M J, The Rib, St Andrew Street, Wells BA5 2UR
Child Evangelism Fellowship, c/o 64 Osborne Road, Levenshulme, Manchester M19 2DY
Christian Music Ministries, 325 Bromfield Road, Hodge Hill, Birmingham B36 8ET
Cooke, N A M, PO Box 201, West Malling, Kent ME19 5RS
CopyCare Ltd, PO Box 77, Hailsham, East Sussex BN27 3EF
Crabtree, Roy, 7 Ascot Court, Carmen Sylva Road, Craig-y-don, Llandudno, Gwynedd LL30 1LZ
Daybreak Music Ltd, Silverdale Road, Eastbourne, East Sussex BN20 7AB
Dudley-Smith, Timothy, 9 Ashlands, Ford, Salisbury, Wilts SP4 6DY
Franciscan Communications, 1229 South Santee Street, Los Angeles, California 90015, USA
Gill, D M, Kerry Hill, Hawling, Andoversford, Glos GL54 5SZ
Hall, Archie, Lochinver, 69 King George V Avenue, King's Lynn, Norfolk PE30 2QE
HarperCollins*Religious*, c/o CopyCare Ltd, PO Box 77, Hailsham, East Sussex BN27 3EF
Herald Music Service, 28 Church Circle, Farnborough, Hants
David Higham Associates, 5-8 Lower John Street, Golden Square, London W1R 4HA
High-Fye Music, Campbell Connelly & Co Ltd, 8-9 Frith Street, London W1V 5TZ
Hooke, Ruth, 10 Bridgeway, Lostock Hall, Preston, Lancs PR5 5YJ
Horrobin, P J, Ellel Grange, Ellel, Carnforth, Lancs LA2 0HN
Hughes, Andy, c/o Holmleigh, 8 Church Road, Upton, Wirral, Merseyside L49 6JZ
Hutchinson, G E, 158 Lansdowne Road, Worcester WR3 8JA
Jubilate Hymns, c/o Mrs Bunty Grundy, 13 Stoddart Avenue, Southampton SO19 4ED
Keats, Carolyn, 12 Salisbury Road, Swanage, Dorset DH19 2DY
Kerr, B K M, Wayside Cottage, East Dean, Eastbourne, East Sussex BN20 0BP
Kersys, Steve, 136 Main Road, Danbury, Essex CM3 4DT
Kingsway's Thankyou Music, PO Box 75, Eastbourne, East Sussex BN23 6NW
Leavers, Greg, 1 Haws Hill, Carnforth, Lancs LA5 9DD
Leosong Copyright Service Ltd, Greenland Place, 115-123 Bayham Street, Camden, London NW1 0AG
Lewis, Peter, 22 Marlborough Rise, Aston, Sheffield S31 0ET
Lindsay Music, 23 Hitchin Street, Biggleswade, Beds SG18 8AX
Little Misty Music, PO Box 8, Perth, Scotland PH2 7EX
Make Way Music Ltd, PO Box 263, Croydon, Surrey CR9 5AP
Kevin Mayhew Ltd, The Paddock, Rattlesden, Bury St Edmunds, Suffolk IP30 0SZ
McCrimmon Publishing Company, 10-12 High Street, Great Wakering, Essex SS3 0EQ
Meredith, Rev Roland, 1 Deanery Court, Broad Street, Bampton, Oxon OX18 2LY
Methodist Church Publishing House, 20 Ivatt Way, Peterborough, Cambs PE3 7PG
National Christian Education Council, 1020 Bristol Road, Selly Oak, Birmingham B29 6LB
Oaksprings Impressions, PO Box 394, Fairfax, California 94930, USA
Oxford University Press, Hymn Copyright Department, 70 Baker Street, London W1M 1DJ
Reith, Angela, 47 Mayton Street, London N7 6QP
Robinson, Joan, 47 Woodlands Road, Beaumont, Lancaster LA1 2EH
Scarr, S Lesley, 15 Church Park, Overton, Morecambe LA3 3RA
Scripture Gift Mission, Radstock House, 3 Eccleston Street, London SW1W 9LZ
Scripture Press Publications, 1825 College Avenue, Wheaton, Illinois 60187, USA
Scripture Union, 207-9 Queensway, Bletchley, Bucks MK2 2EB
Sea Dream Music, 236 Sabert Road, Forest Gate, London E7 0NP
Silver, Andy, Bell House Farm, Dalton, Burton-in-Kendal, Lancs LA6 1NN
Simmonds, C, School House, 81 Clapham Road, Bedford MK41 7RB
Stainer & Bell Ltd, PO Box 110, 23 Gruneisen Road, London N3 1DZ
Taylor, P A, 1 The Baulk, Worksop, Notts S81 0HU
Waif Productions, 1 North Worple Way, Mortlake, London SW14 8QG
Josef Weinberger Ltd, 12-14 Mortimer Street, London W1N 7RD
Westworth, M, 3 Greengate Lane, Crag Bank, Carnforth, Lancs LA5 9JJ

Subject Index

A: SEASONAL

1 Advent
Bring your Christingle 315
God whose love is everywhere 353
Hark, the glad sound 68
Hey! Hey! Anybody listening 362
How lovely on the mountains 84
It's rounded like an orange 402
Jesus, how lovely You are 133
Make way, make way 427
Mighty in victory 430
O come, O come, Emmanuel 177
O when the saints go marching in 195
On Jordan's bank the Baptist's cry 186
Our eyes have seen the glory 191
Sing we the King 218
Soon and very soon 221
When the Lord in glory comes 280
When the trumpet of the Lord 281

2 Ascension
At the name of Jesus 13
Christ triumphant 25
It's easy to be a believer 400
Jesus Christ is alive today 129

3 Christmas
A special star 305
Angels from the realms of glory 10
As with gladness 9
Away in a manger 12
Born in the night 313
Christmas is a time to love 321
Christmas isn't Christmas 322
Come and join the celebration 323
Come and praise the Lord our King 34
Come on and celebrate 325
Crackers and turkeys 327
Ding dong! Merrily on high 38
From heaven You came 341
Girls and boys, leave your toys 344
Glory to God in the highest 51
Hark! the herald-angels sing 69
Infant holy 110
It came upon the midnight clear 116
It was on a starry night 396
Jesus Christ the Lord is born 131
Long ago there was born 418
Mary had a little baby 164
O come, all ye faithful 176
O little town of Bethlehem 182
On Christmas night 441
Once in royal David's city 185
See, amid the winter snow 213
See Him lying on a bed of straw 214
See, to us a Child is born 452
Silent night 219
Sing and celebrate (Christmas) 456
The first nowell 238
The shepherds found 471

The virgin Mary had a baby boy 251
This Child 480
Unto us a boy is born! 263
We three kings 271
While shepherds watched 285

4 Easter and Holy Week
A purple robe 304
Alleluia, alleluia 3
Barabbas was a bad man 18
Children, join the celebration 320
From heaven You came 341
God sent His Son 58
God's not dead 60
He is Lord, He is Lord 75
He paid a debt 77
I danced in the morning 91
I met You at the cross 103
I serve a risen Saviour 113
I will sing the wondrous story 127
It is a thing most wonderful 117
It's easy to be a believer 400
Jesus Christ is alive today 129
Jesus Christ is risen today 130
Jesus died for all the children 132
Jesus is Lord 137
Led like a lamb 151
Live, live, live 153
Low in the grave He lay 159
O the love that drew salvation's plan 181
Oh, how He loves you and me 436
Oh, oh, oh, oh 438
On Calvary's tree 183
One day when heaven 187
Roll the stone 449
Saviour of the world 216
Sing and celebrate (Easter) 457
The Lord is risen today 469
The Spirit lives 472
There is a green hill 245
This joyful Eastertide 256
Were you there? 269
What a wonderful Saviour 274
When I survey 277
Yours be the glory 299

5 Harvest
At harvest time 311
Come, you thankful people, come 32
For the beauty of the earth 48
God in His love for us 347
God who made the earth 63
God, whose farm is all creation 61
Great is Your faithfulness 64
I have seen the golden sunshine 99
It takes an almighty hand 395
Jesus is Lord 137
Now thank we all our God 175
Now the green blade riseth 174
Our harvest day is over 193
Someone's brought a loaf of bread 220

Think of a world without any flowers 254
What colours God has made 488
What drives the stars 490
When Israel was in Egypt's land 276
When we look up 495
Yes, God is good 293

6 Lent
All you have to do 307
Dear Lord and Father of mankind 37
Father, hear the prayer we offer 41
Father, lead me day by day 43
God of all mercy 350
I'm feeding on the living bread 104
I've come to a time 383
Let us praise God together 152
Sometimes I'm naughty 460
Sorry, Lord 463

7 Palm Sunday
Children of Jerusalem 24
Going up to Jerusalem 354
Hosanna, hosanna 365
Make way, make way 427
Ride on, ride on 209
We have a king who rides a donkey 264

8 Pentecost (Whitsun)
All over the world 5
For I'm building a people of power 47
God whose Son was once a man 62
I am the Church 367
Jesus, send me the helper 409
Spirit of God 465
Spirit of the living God 222
The Spirit lives 472
When God breathes 497

B: THE GODHEAD

9 God the Father
Abba Father 2
Be still and know 22
Can you imagine 318
Dear Lord and Father of mankind 37
Father God, I wonder 337
Father, hear the prayer we offer 41
Father, I place into Your hands 42
Father, lead me day by day 43
Father, we adore You 44
Father, we love You 45
Father, Your word 338
For the foolishness of God 340
God has made me 346
God is good 55
God is our guide 56
God is so good 53
God is working His purpose out 57
God loves you 348
God loves you so much 349
God of all mercy 350
God was there 352

God whose love is everywhere 353
God's not dead 60
Grace is 355
Great is Your faithfulness 64
Hallelujah! for the Lord our God 66
He brought me to His banqueting house 73
He's got the whole wide world 78
He's great! He's God 79
How great is our God 82
How lovely on the mountains 84
I am so glad 88
I'm very glad of God 107
I'm going to take a step of faith 381
It takes an almighty hand 395
It's not very nice saying 401
Jehovah Jireh 404
Let us praise God together 152
Let us with a gladsome mind 154
Lord, You are brilliant 423
Mighty is our God 431
My God is so big 169
Now thank we all our God 175
O Lord my God! 179
O Lord, You're great 435
Our Father who is in heaven 192
Praise God, from whom all blessings flow 199
Praise to the Lord our God 205
Sing a new song to the Lord 454
Stand up and bless the Lord 224
Standing in Your presence, Lord 466
The joy of the Lord is my strength 240
The King of love 241
The Lord's my shepherd 243
The steadfast love 250
There is no-one else 476
To God be the glory! 259
What a mighty God we serve 491
What colours God has made 488
Yes, God is good 293
You are holy 500

10   Jesus
A boy gave to Jesus 1
Alleluia 308
Alleluia, alleluia 3
At the name of Jesus 13
Bless the Lord, O my soul 19
Blesséd assurance 20
By blue Galilee 23
Can you count the stars 317
Christ triumphant 25
Come and praise the Lord our King 34
Come on and celebrate 325
Come to Jesus, He's amazing 33
Do you want a pilot? 40
Father, we adore You 44
Father, we love You 45
'Follow Me,' says Jesus 46
From heaven You came 341
God sent His Son 58
Going up to Jerusalem 354
Happiness is to know the Saviour 70
He is Lord, He is Lord 75
I am the resurrection 368

I am the way, the truth and the life 89
I am trusting You 86
Jesus has promised 406
I danced in the morning 91
I have a friend 370
I love You, Lord Jesus 372
I serve a risen Saviour 113
I was lost but Jesus found me 125
I will sing the wondrous story 127
If Jesus is de vine 386
If you climb 388
In the name of Jesus 111
It was Jesus who taught 397
It's easy to be a believer 400
Jesus bids us shine 128
Jesus Christ is alive today 129
Jesus Christ is risen today 130
Jesus died for all the children 132
Jesus has promised 406
Jesus, how lovely You are 133
Jesus is a friend of mine 136
Jesus is Lord 137
Jesus loves me 140
Jesus, name above all names 141
Jesus, Prince and Saviour 407
Jesus put this song into our hearts 408
Jesus, send me the helper 409
Jesus was the Son of God 411
Jesus will never, ever 412
Jesus' hands were kind hands 134
Jesus' love is very wonderful 139
King of kings and Lord of lords 148
Led like a lamb 151
Let's talk about Jesus 150
Lord Jesus Christ 156
Lord Jesus, You are faithful 420
Lord of all hopefulness 157
Lord, You are the Light 424
Majesty 160
Make way, make way 427
May the mind of Christ my Saviour 165
Mighty in victory 430
My Lord is higher than a mountain 170
O! O! O! how good is the Lord 180
Oh, how He loves you and me 436
Oh, oh, oh, oh 438
Oh, yes I am 439
On Calvary's tree 183
Once there was a house 444
Our eyes have seen the glory 191
Praise Him, praise Him 203
Praise, my soul, the King of heaven 204
Saviour of the world 216
See the man walking 451
Shine bright 453
Sing we the King 218
Soon and very soon 221
Tell me the old, old, story 227
Tell me the stories of Jesus 228
Thank You, thank You, Jesus 231
The Spirit lives 472
Turn your eyes upon Jesus 260
We have a king who rides a donkey 264

We love to praise You 265
We'll praise Him on the trumpet 486
What a friend we have in Jesus 273
What a wonderful Saviour 274
When I'm feeling lonely 493
When the Lord in glory comes 280
When we look up 495
Who took fish and bread 286
Yesterday, today, for ever 294
You are the King of glory 296
You can't catch a plane 502
You're my maker 503

11   The Holy Spirit
All over the world 5
For I'm building a people of power 47
Give me oil in my lamp 50
God whose Son was once a man 62
Hang on 356
I am a lighthouse 87
I want to walk with Jesus 124
Jesus, send me the helper 409
Love, joy, peace 425
Love, joy, peace and patience 158
Spirit of God 465
Spirit of the living God 222
Thank You, God, for sending Jesus 233
The Spirit lives 472
This is the day 255
Though the world has forsaken God 257
When God breathes 497
Wherever I am I will praise You 283

12   The Trinity
Father, we adore You 44
Father, we love You 45
I'm going to shine, shine, shine 392
Praise God, from whom all blessings flow 199
Sing praise 455
Thank You, God, for sending Jesus 233
We really want to thank You, Lord 268

C: SUBJECT HEADINGS

13   Bible and Scripture songs
A new commandment 303
Are you humbly grateful 309
Ask! Ask! Ask! 11
Be still and know 22
Behold, what manner of love 15
Father, Your word 338
God loves you so much 349
God so loved the world 59
Have you got an appetite 357
He brought me to His banqueting house 73
He gives me strength 360
How lovely on the mountains 84
I am the resurrection 368
I am the way, the truth and the life 89
I will make you fishers of men 123
I'm going to hide God's word inside my heart 378

I'm going to say my prayers 379
I'm going to set my heart 382
If you love Me 387
If your empty tum 390
Jesus, I will come with You 138
Make the book live to me 163
Now be strong 172
Search me, O God 212
Seek ye first 215
Surely goodness and mercy 223
Tell me the old, old story 227
Tell me the stories of Jesus 228
The best book to read 234
The joy of the Lord is my strength 240
The Lord's my shepherd 243
The word of the Lord is planted 473
The word of God 474
We need to grow 484

14   Bible story songs
A boy gave to Jesus 1
Are you humbly grateful 309
Barabbas was a bad man 18
Big man 16
By blue Galilee 23
Children of Jerusalem 24
Come, listen to my tale 30
Come to Jesus, He's amazing 33
Daniel was a man of prayer 36
Don't build your house on the sandy land 39
God told Joshua 351
His name was Saul 363
How did Moses cross the Red Sea? 83
Hushed was the evening hymn 85
I look out through the doorway 371
If you love Me 387
Isaiah heard the voice of the Lord 114
It was Jesus who taught 397
Jerusalem man 405
Joseph was sold as a slave 413
Joshua fit the battle of Jericho 143
Long, long ago 419
Matthew had been sitting 428
Mister Noah built an ark 167
M-m-m-m-must I really go 426
Noah was the only good man 432
Now Saul was rejected 433
Oh no! The wine's all gone 437
Oh, the Lord looked down 184
Old man Noah 440
On Jordan's bank the Baptist's cry 186
On the road to Damascus 442
Once there was a house 444
Once upon a time 443
One and two and three and four 445
Only a boy called David 190
Peter and James and John 197
Peter and John 198
Said Judas to Mary 211
Saul had made himself 450
See the man walking 451
Six hundred years old 458
Spies were sent out 464
Tell me the stories of Jesus 228

The wise man built his house upon the rock 252
There he stood - Goliath 475
There once was a man 477
Twelve men went to spy 261
Wandering like lost sheep 482
We have a king who rides a donkey 264
What made a difference 492
When Israel was in Egypt's land 276
Who took fish and bread 286
Zacchaeus was a very little man 300

15   Blessings and the doxology
Lord, dismiss us 155
Lord, we ask now 301
Praise God, from whom all blessings flow 199
Shalom, my friend 217

16   Christian living
Abba Father 2
And we know that all things 310
Are you humbly grateful 309
Be bold, be strong 14
Be careful, little hands 312
Be holy 314
Bind us together, Lord 17
Christ be my leader 319
Come on, let's get up and go 31
Do you want a pilot? 40
Don't build your house on the sandy land 39
Even if I don't 330
Every day if you go astray 331
Everywhere He walks with me 334
From heaven You came 341
Give me oil in my lamp 50
God forgave my sin 54
God whose Son was once a man 62
He gives me strength 360
He who would valiant be 80
His ways are not our ways 364
I am trusting You 86
I can run through a troop 90
I do not know what lies ahead 92
I have a friend 370
I have decided to follow Jesus 98
I want to live for Jesus every day 122
I want to walk with Jesus 124
I'm going to say my prayers 370
I'm going to shine, shine, shine 392
I'm going to stand up 380
I'm going to take a step of faith 381
I've got peace like a river 120
I've got that joy, joy, joy, joy 121
If you climb 388
If you see someone 95
If you want to be great 389
In everything that I do 391
In our work and in our play 108
It's a happy day 118
It's an adventure 399
It's not very nice saying 401
It's the little things 403
Jesus, send me the helper 409
Just as I am 146
Keep me shining, Lord 147
Kids under construction 414

Lord, make me a mountain 421
Love, joy, peace 425
Make me a channel of Your peace 161
Make me a servant, Lord 162
May the mind of Christ my Saviour 165
My faith is like a staff of oak 168
Now be strong 172
Oh, yes I am 439
One more step along the world I go 188
Peace I give to you 196
Sometimes problems 461
Spirit of the living God 222
Stand up! stand up for Jesus 226
The greatest thing in all my life 239
The joy of the Lord is my strength 240
The Lord has need of me 242
The Lord is my shepherd 244
The wise man built his house upon the rock 252
The wise may bring 253
There's new life in Jesus 249
This little light of mine 258
Though the world has forsaken God 257
Turn your eyes upon Jesus 260
We are soldiers of the King 483
We need to grow 484
We're following Jesus 487
When I needed a neighbour 275
When I'm feeling lonely 493
When the dark clouds 494
When the road is rough and steep 279
Wherever I am 282
Wherever I am I will praise 283
Who is on the Lord's side 287
Will your anchor hold 290
Your ways are higher than mine 295

17   The Church
A new commandment 303
All over the world 5
Bind us together, Lord 17
Brothers and sisters 21
For I'm building a people of power 47
God is working His purpose out 57
God loves you 348
I am the Church 367
I hear the sound 100
I may never march in the infantry 101
I sing a song of the saints of God 115
Jesus put this song into our hearts 408
Mighty in victory 430
O when the saints go marching in 195
Saul had made himself 450
So we're marching along 459
Some people laugh 462
Stand up! stand up for Jesus 226
We are soldiers of the King 483
We really want to thank You, Lord 268

Your hand, O God, has guided 298

18 Commitment (dedication)
Abba Father 2
All you have to do 307
Blessèd assurance 20
Do you want a pilot? 40
Father, I place into Your hands 42
Father, lead me day by day 43
Father, we adore You 44
I am trusting You 86
I cast all my cares upon You 369
I have decided to follow Jesus 98
I met Jesus at the crossroads 102
I met You at the cross 103
I want to live for Jesus every day 122
I want to love You, Lord 374
I want to walk with Jesus Christ 124
I'm going to take a step of faith 381
I've come to a time 383
If any man come after Me 384
If it pleases the King 385
Into my heart 394
It's easy to be a believer 400
Jesus has promised 406
Jesus is knocking 135
Jesus, I will come with You 138
Just as I am 146
Lord, we ask now 301
Maybe you can't draw or sing 429
Spirit of the living God 222
The journey of life 468
The Lord has need of me 242
The most important thing 470
There's a way back 248
We're following Jesus 487
What do you give 489
What made a difference 492
When I survey 277
When You're feeling good 496
Who is on the Lord's side 287
Will your anchor hold 290
Would you walk by 498
Yet to all who received Him 499

19 Confession
All you have to do 307
Cleanse me from my sin 27
God of all mercy 350
Search me, O God 212
Sometimes I'm naughty 460
Sorry, Lord 463
Spirit of the living God 222

20 Friends and family
naggy mum 302
Bind us together, Lord 17
Brothers and sisters 21
Father, I place into Your hands 42
For the beauty of the earth 48
Have you seen the pussycat 72
He's got the whole wide world 78
In our work and in our play 108
Is me, it's me 119
Jesus is a friend of mine 136
Lord, we ask now 301
Shalom, my friend 217
Thank You for the love 467
When we look up 495

21 God in creation
All around me, Lord 7
All things bright and beautiful 6
Can you count the stars 317
Can you imagine 318
Counting, counting, one, two, three 326
Don't know much 329
For the beauty of the earth 48
For the foolishness of God 340
God in His love for us 347
God who made the earth 63
God, whose farm is all creation 61
He made the stars to shine 76
He made the water wet 359
In the stars His handiwork I see 112
It came upon the midnight clear 116
Large creatures 415
Long, long ago 419
Mighty is our God 431
O Lord my God! 179
Remember all the people 207
Stand up, clap hands 225
What colours God has made 488
What do you give 489
What drives the stars 490
When we look up 495
Who put the colours in the rainbow? 288

22 Guidance
And we know that all things 310
Ask! Ask! Ask! 11
Be bold, be strong 14
Christ be my leader 319
Do you want a pilot? 40
Father, I place into Your hands 42
Father, lead me day by day 43
God is our guide 56
God is working His purpose out 57
His ways are not our ways 364
I am trusting You 86
I do not know what lies ahead 92
I have decided to follow Jesus 98
I'm going to take a step of faith 381
In everything that I do 391
It's an adventure 399
One more step along the world I go 188
Spies were sent out 464
The journey of life 468
The Lord's my shepherd 243
There's a song for all the children 478
We're following Jesus 487
When the road is rough and steep 279
Will your anchor hold 290
Your hand, O God, has guided 298

23 Health and healing
Be still and know 22
Cleanse me from my sin 27
Come to Jesus, He's amazing 33
Dear Lord and Father of mankind 37
I cast all my cares upon You 360
In the name of Jesus 111
Jehovah Jireh 404
Live, live, live 153

Make me a channel of Your peace 161
May the mind of Christ my Saviour 165
O! O! O! how good is the Lord 180
Oh, how He loves you and me 436
Peace I give to you 196
Peter and John 198
There's new life in Jesus 249
Turn your eyes upon Jesus 260

24 Missions home and abroad
All over the world 5
Can you imagine 318
Colours of day 28
Come, let us sing 29
Come on, let's get up and go 31
Come to Jesus, He's amazing 33
Father, I place into Your hands 42
For I'm building a people of power 47
Go, tell it on the mountain 65
God forgave my sin 54
God is working His purpose out 57
How lovely on the mountains 84
I serve a risen Saviour 113
I will make you fishers of men 123
I'm going to stand up 380
I'm singing for my Lord 105
Isaiah heard the voice of the Lord 114
Jesus bids us shine 128
Joy is the flag 144
Let's go and tell our friends 416
Let's talk about Jesus 150
Make me a channel of Your peace 161
Make way, make way 427
Remember all the people 207
Stand up! stand up for Jesus 226
Tell out, my soul 229
The fields are white 237
There's a song for all the children 478
This little light of mine 258
Though the world has forsaken God 257
We have heard a joyful sound 266
We've a story to tell 272
When I needed a neighbour 275

25 Morning and evening
Get up out of bed 343
Glory to You, my God 52
Hushed was the evening hymn 85
I'm going to say my prayers 379
In the morning 393
It's a happy day 118
Lord, dismiss us 155
Lord of all hopefulness 157
Lord, we ask now 301
Morning has broken 166
New every morning is the love 171
Now the day is over 173
Praise Him, praise Him, praise Him in the morning 202
Thank You, Lord, for this fine day 232
The day You gave us 236
This is the day 255
When morning gilds the skies 278

26 Praise and worship

Abba Father	2
All people that on earth do dwell	4
All things bright and beautiful	6
Alleluia	308
Alleluia, alleluia, give thanks	3
Amazing grace	8
At the name of Jesus	13
Bless the Lord, O my soul	19
Blessèd assurance	20
Christ triumphant	25
Clap your hands, all you people	26
Come and praise the Lord our King	34
Come, let us sing	29
Come, let us sing for joy	324
Come on and celebrate	325
Dear Lord and Father of mankind	37
Even if I don't	330
Everybody join in singing	332
Father God, I wonder	337
Father, we adore You	44
Father, we love You	45
Fill your hearts with joy	339
For the beauty of the earth	48
From the rising of the sun	49
Give thanks to the Lord	345
God is good	55
God is so good	53
God is working His purpose out	57
God who made the earth	63
Great is Your faithfulness	64
Hallelu, hallelu	67
Hallelujah! for the Lord our God	66
Happiness is to know the Saviour	70
He is Lord, He is Lord	75
He's got the whole wide world	78
He's great! He's God	79
Hosanna, hosanna	365
How great is our God	82
How lovely on the mountains	84
I am so glad	88
I can run through a troop	90
I love You, Lord Jesus	372
I serve a risen Saviour	113
I want to love You, Lord	374
I was lost but Jesus found me	125
I will sing, I will sing	126
I will sing the wondrous story	127
I will wave my hands	376
I'll be still	93
I'm very glad of God	107
I've got peace like a river	120
I've got that joy, joy, joy, joy	121
In my need Jesus found me	109
In the name of Jesus	111
In the stars His handiwork I see	112
It is a thing most wonderful	117
It's a song of praise	398
Jesus Christ is alive today	129
Jesus, how lovely You are	133
Jesus, I love You	410
Jesus is Lord	137
Jesus loves me	140
Jesus, name above all names	141
Jesus will never, ever	412
Jesus' love is very wonderful	139
Jubilate, everybody	145
King of kings and Lord of lords	148

Led like a lamb	151
Let us praise God together	152
Let us with a gladsome mind	154
Let's praise God together	417
Let's talk about Jesus	150
Lord Jesus Christ	156
Lord of all hopefulness	157
Lord Jesus, You are faithful	420
Lord, we've come to worship You	422
Lord, You are brilliant	423
Lord, You are the Light	424
Majesty	160
Mighty is our God	431
My faith is like a staff of oak	168
My God is so big	169
New every morning	171
Now thank we all our God	175
O give thanks to the Lord	434
O Lord my God!	179
O Lord, You're great	435
O! O! O! how good is the Lord	180
Oh, how He loves you and me	436
Oh, oh, oh, oh	438
Oh, yes I am	439
One day when heaven	187
Our eyes have seen the glory	191
Praise and thanksgiving	447
Praise Him	446
Praise Him on the trumpet	200
Praise Him, praise Him	203
Praise Him, praise Him, all you little children	201
Praise Him, praise, Him, praise Him in the morning	202
Praise, my soul, the King of heaven	204
Praise to the Lord our God	205
Rejoice in the Lord always	208
Sing a new song to the Lord	454
Sing praise	455
Sing we the King	218
Some people laugh	462
Stand up and bless the Lord	224
Stand up, clap hands	225
Stand up! stand up for Jesus	226
Standing in Your presence, Lord	466
Tell me the old, old story	227
Tell me the stories of Jesus	228
Tell out, my soul	229
Thank You	230
Thank You, God, for sending Jesus	233
Thank You, Jesus	235
Thank You, Lord, for this fine day	232
Thank You, thank You, Jesus	231
The greatest thing	239
The joy of the Lord is my strength	240
The King of love my shepherd is	241
The Lord is my shepherd	244
The Lord's my shepherd	243
The steadfast love	250
There's a song of exaltation	247
There's new life in Jesus	249
Think big: an elephant	479
This is a catchy songa	481
This is the day	255

To God be the glory!	259
We have heard a joyful sound	266
We love to praise You	265
We really want to thank You, Lord	268
We will praise	485
We'll praise Him on the trumpet	486
We've a story to tell	272
What a friend we have in Jesus	273
What a mighty God we serve	491
What a wonderful Saviour	274
When I survey	277
Wherever I am	282
Wherever I am I will praise You	283
Will your anchor hold	290
Yes, God is good	293
Yesterday, today, forever	294
You are the King of glory	296
You are holy	500
You're my maker	503
Your ways are higher	295
Yours be the glory	299

27 Prayers and songs about prayer

Abba Father	2
All you have to do	307
Ask! Ask! Ask!	11
Cleanse me from my sin	27
Daniel was a man of prayer	36
Did you ever talk to God above	329
Father, hear the prayer we offer	41
Father, I place into Your hands	42
Father, lead me day by day	43
God has made me	346
His ways are not our ways	364
I cast all my cares upon You	369
I want to love You, Lord	374
I'm going to say my prayers	379
Into my heart	394
Jesus, send me the helper	409
Lord, make me a mountain	421
Our Father who is in heaven	192
Peter and John	198
Prayer is like a telephone	448
Spirit of God	465
Spirit of the living God	222
Thank You, God, for sending Jesus	233
What a friend we have in Jesus	273
When I'm feeling lonely	493
When the dark clouds	494

28 Rounds and part songs

All around me, Lord	7
Brothers and sisters	21
Clap your hands, all you people	26
Come, let us sing for joy	324
Don't build your house on the sandy land	39
Father, we adore You	44
God of all mercy	356
Hey, you, do you love Jesus	361
I love You, Lord Jesus	372
I want to tell You	375
I was lost but Jesus found me	125
If any man come after Me	38
Jesus, I will come with You	131
King of kings and Lord of lords	148

Oh, oh, oh, oh 438
Peace I give to you 196
Praise and thanksgiving 447
Praise Him on the trumpet 200
Rejoice in the Lord always 208
See the man walking 451
Seek ye first 215
Shalom, my friend 217
Sing and celebrate (Christmas) 456
Sing and celebrate (Easter) 457
The Lord is my shepherd 244
The Lord is risen today 469
There's a song of exaltation 247

29   Service and giving

A boy gave to Jesus 1
Be bold, be strong 14
Father, I place into Your hands 42
Give me oil in my lamp 50
God forgave my sin 54
He gave me eyes so I could see 74
He gives me strength 360
I am a lighthouse 87
I sing a song of the saints of God 115
I want to love You, Lord 374
I'm going to shine, shine, shine 392
I'm going to stand up 380
If it pleases the King 385
If you see someone 95
If you want to be great 389
It's an adventure 399
It's the little things 403
Jesus bids us shine 128
Jubilate, everybody 145
Lord, make me a mountain 421
Lord, we ask now 301
Make me a channel of Your peace 161
Make me a servant, Lord 162
May the mind of Christ my Saviour 165
M-m-m-m-must I really go 426
One more step along the world I go 188
Peace I give to you 196
Spies were sent out 464
The greatest thing in all my life 239
The Lord has need of me 242
There's new life in Jesus 249
We're following Jesus 487
What do you give 489
When I needed a neighbour 275
Who is on the Lord's side 287
Would you walk by 498

30   Songs suitable for the very young

A naggy mum 302
A wiggly waggly worm 306
Alleluia 308
Away in a manger 12
Be careful, little hands 312

Brothers and sisters 21
Come and praise the Lord our King 34
Daniel was a man of prayer 36
Deep and wide 35
Everyone in the whole wide world 333
Father, we adore You 44
From my knees to my nose 342
Give thanks to the Lord 345
God is so good 53
God loves you 348
God so loved the world 59
Hallelu, hallelu 67
Have you seen the pussycat 72
He made the water wet 359
How did Moses cross the Red Sea? 83
I am like a house 366
I may never march in the infantry 101
I will make you fishers of men 123
I'm special 106
If I were a butterfly 94
In our work and in our play 108
Jesus bids us shine 128
Jesus is a friend of mine 136
Jesus loves me 140
Jesus' hands were kind hands 134
Jesus' love is very wonderful 139
Joy is the flag 144
Lord, we've come to worship You 422
Mister Noah built an ark 167
My God is so big 169
O! O! O! how good is the Lord 180
Oh, how He loves you and me 436
One, two, three, Jesus loves me 189
Only a boy called David 190
Praise Him 446
Praise Him, praise Him, all you little children 201
Shalom, my friend 217
So we're marching along 459
Thank You, Lord, for this fine day 232
The best book to read 234
The wise man built his house upon the rock 252
This is a catchy songa 481
This little light of mine 258
Two little eyes 262
We have a king who rides a donkey 264
Whether you're one 284
Wide, wide as the ocean 292
With Jesus in the boat 291
Zacchaeus was a very little man 300

31   Spirituals

Go, tell it on the mountain 65
He's got the whole wide world 78
I gotta home in gloryland 97

It's me, it's me 119
Joshua fit the battle of Jericho 143
Kum ba yah 149
O sinner man 194
O when the saints go marching in 195
Our Father who is in heaven 192
This little light of mine 258
Were you there? 269
When Israel was in Egypt's land 276

32   Times of sadness

Amazing grace 8
Be still and know 22
Father, be with her family 335
Father, for our friends we pray 336
Father, hear the prayer we offer 41
Father, I place into Your hands 42
God loves you 348
Great is Your faithfulness 64
I am trusting You 86
I cast all my cares upon You 369
I do not know what lies ahead 92
I have a friend 370
I'll be still 93
Jesus loves me 140
Kum ba yah 149
Make me a channel of Your peace 161
Now be strong 172
Shalom, my friend 217
The King of love 241
The Lord's my shepherd 243
The steadfast love 250
Turn your eyes upon Jesus 260
What a friend we have in Jesus 273
When I'm feeling lonely 493
When the dark clouds 494
When you're feeling good 496
Yesterday, today, for ever 294

33   Work and play

Brothers and sisters 21
Father, I place into Your hands 42
Father, lead me day by day 43
From heaven You came 341
I sing a song of the saints of God 115
I want to live for Jesus every day 122
In our work and in our play 108
It's a happy day 118
It's the little things 403
Just as I am 146
The most important thing 470
Though the world has forsaken God 257
When you're feeling good 496
Wherever I am 282
Wherever I am I will praise 283

Index of First Lines

Titles which differ from first lines appear in italics

A boy gave to Jesus	1
A naggy mum	302
A new commandment	303
A purple robe	304
A special star	305
A wiggly waggly worm	306
Abba Father	2
All around me, Lord	7
All over the world	5
All people that on earth do dwell	4
All things bright and beautiful	6
All you have to do	307
Alleluia	308
Alleluia, alleluia	3
Amazing grace	8
And we know that all things	310
Angels from the realms of glory	10
Are you humbly grateful	309
Arky Arky song, the	210
As with gladness	9
Ask! Ask! Ask!	11
At harvest time	311
At the name of Jesus	13
Away in a manger	12
Barabbas was a bad man	18
Be bold, be strong	14
Be careful, little hands	312
Be holy	314
Be still and know	22
Because He lives	58
Behold, what manner of love	15
Big man	16
Bind us together, Lord	17
Bless the Lord, O my soul	19
Blessèd assurance	20
Born in the night	313
Bring your Christingle	315
Brothers and sisters	21
Butterfly song, the	94
By blue Galilee	23
Calypso Carol	214
Can you be sure	316
Can you count the stars	317
Can you imagine	318
Children, join the celebration	320
Children of Jerusalem	24
Christ be my leader	319
Christ triumphant	25
Christmas is a time to love	321
Christmas isn't Christmas	322
Clap your hands, all you people	26
Cleanse me from my sin	27
Colours of day	28
Come and join the celebration	323
Come and praise the Lord our King	34
Come, let us sing	29
Come, let us sing for joy	324
Come, listen to my tale	30
Come on and celebrate	325

Come on, let's get up and go	31
Come to Jesus, He's amazing	33
Come, you thankful people, come	32
Counting, counting, one, two, three	326
Crackers and turkeys	327
Daniel was a man of prayer	36
Dear Lord and Father of mankind	37
Deep and wide	35
Did you ever talk to God above	329
Ding dong! Merrily on high	38
Do you want a pilot?	40
Don't build your house on the sandy land	39
Don't know much	328
Even if I don't	330
Every day if you go astray	331
Everybody join in singing	332
Everyone in the whole wide world	333
Everywhere He walks with me	334
Father, be with her family	335
Father, for our friends we pray	336
Father God, I wonder	337
Father, hear the prayer we offer	41
Father, I place into Your hands	42
Father, lead me day by day	43
Father, we adore You	44
Father, we love You	45
Father, Your word	338
Fill your hearts with joy	339
'Follow Me,' says Jesus	46
For I'm building a people of power	47
For the beauty of the earth	48
For the foolishness of God	340
Freely, freely	54
From heaven You came	341
From my knees to my nose	342
From the rising of the sun	49
Get up out of bed	343
Girls and boys, leave your toys	344
Give me oil in my lamp	50
Give thanks to the Lord	345
Glory to God in the highest	51
Glory to You, my God	52
Go, tell it on the mountain	65
God forgave my sin	54
God has made me	346
God in His love for us	347
God is good	55
God is our guide	56
God is so good	53
God is working His purpose out	57
God loves you	348
God loves you so much	349
God of all mercy	350
God sent His Son	58
God so loved the world	59

God told Joshua	351
God was there	352
God who made the earth	63
God, whose farm is all creation	61
God whose love is everywhere	353
God whose Son was once a man	62
God's not dead	60
Going up to Jerusalem	354
Grace is	355
Great is Your faithfulness	64
Hallelu, hallelu	67
Hallelujah! for the Lord our God	66
Hang on	356
Happiness is to know the Saviour	70
Hark, the glad sound	68
Hark! the herald-angels sing	69
Have you got an appetite	357
Have you heard the raindrops	71
Have you seen the pussycat	72
He brought me to His banqueting house	73
He gave me eyes so I could see	74
He gives me strength	366
He is Lord, He is Lord	75
He lives	113
He made the stars to shine	76
He made the water wet	351
He paid a debt	77
He who would valiant be	80
He's got the whole wide world	77
He's great! He's God	77
Heavenly Father	35
Hévénu shalom	80
Hey! Hey! Anybody listening	360
Hey, you, do you love Jesus	360
His banner over me is love	73
His name was Saul	36
His ways are not our ways	36
Hosanna, hosanna	36
How did Moses cross the Red Sea?	80
How great is our God	80
How lovely on the mountains	8
Hushed was the evening hymn	8
I am a lighthouse	8
I am a sheep	37
I am like a house	36
I am so glad	8
I am the Church	36
I am the resurrection	8
I am the way, the truth and the life	8
I am trusting You	8
I can run through a troop	9
I cast all my cares upon You	36
I danced in the morning	9
I do not know what lies ahead	9
I gotta home in gloryland	9
I have a friend	3
I have decided to follow Jesus	9
I have seen the golden sunshine	9

Title	Page
I hear the sound	100
I look out through the doorway	371
I love You, Lord Jesus	372
I may never march in the infantry	101
I met Jesus at the crossroads	102
I met You at the cross	103
I serve a risen Saviour	113
I sing a song of the saints of God	115
I want to live for Jesus every day	122
I want to love You, Lord	374
I want to tell you	375
I want to walk with Jesus	124
I was lost but Jesus found me	125
I will make you fishers of men	123
I will sing, I will sing	126
I will sing the wondrous story	127
I will wave my hands	376
I'll be still	93
I'm a footstep follower	377
I'm feeding on the living bread	104
I'm going to hide God's word inside my heart	378
I'm going to say my prayers	379
I'm going to set my heart	382
I'm going to shine, shine, shine	392
I'm going to stand up	380
I'm going to take a step of faith	381
I'm singing for my Lord	105
I'm special	106
I'm very glad of God	107
I've come to a time	383
I've got peace like a river	120
I've got that joy, joy, joy, joy	121
If any man come after Me	384
If I were a butterfly	94
If it pleases the King	385
If Jesus is de vine	386
If you climb	388
If you love Me	387
If you see someone	95
If you want joy, real joy	96
If you want to be great	389
If your empty tum	390
In everything that I do	391
In my need Jesus found me	109
In our work and in our play	108
In the morning	393
In the name of Jesus	111
In the stars His handiwork I see	112
Infant holy	110
Into my heart	394
Isaiah heard the voice of the Lord	114
It came upon the midnight clear	116
It is a thing most wonderful	117
It takes an almighty hand	395
It was Jesus who taught	397
It was on a starry night	396
It's a happy day	118
It's a song of praise	398
It's an adventure	399
It's easy to be a believer	400
It's me, it's me	119
It's not very nice saying	401
It's rounded like an orange	402
It's the little things	403
Jehovah Jireh	404
Jerusalem man	405
Jesus bids us shine	128
Jesus Christ is alive today	129
Jesus Christ is risen today	130
Jesus Christ the Lord is born	131
Jesus died for all the children	132
Jesus has promised	406
Jesus, how lovely You are	133
Jesus, I love You	410
Jesus, I will come with You	138
Jesus is a friend of mine	136
Jesus is knocking	135
Jesus is Lord	137
Jesus loves me	140
Jesus, name above all names	141
Jesus, Prince and Saviour	407
Jesus put this song into our hearts	408
Jesus said that whosoever will	142
Jesus, send me the helper	409
Jesus was the Son of God	411
Jesus will never, ever	412
Jesus' hands were kind hands	134
Jesus' love is very wonderful	139
Joseph was sold as a slave	413
Joshua fit the battle of Jericho	143
Joy is the flag	144
Jubilate, everybody	145
Just as I am	146
Keep me shining, Lord	147
Kids under construction	414
King of kings and Lord of lords	148
Kum ba yah	149
Large creatures	415
Led like a lamb	151
Let us praise God together	152
Let us with a gladsome mind	154
Let's go and tell our friends	416
Let's praise God together	417
Let's talk about Jesus	150
Light up the fire	28
Live, live, live	153
Long ago there was born	418
Long, long ago	419
Lord, dismiss us	155
Lord Jesus Christ	156
Lord Jesus, You are faithful	420
Lord, make me a mountain	421
Lord of all hopefulness	157
Lord of the dance	91
Lord, we ask now	301
Lord, we've come to worship You	422
Lord, You are brilliant	423
Lord, You are the Light	424
Love, joy, peace	425
Love, joy, peace and patience	158
Low in the grave He lay	159
Majesty	160
Make me a channel of Your peace	161
Make me a servant, Lord	162
Make the book live to me	163
Make way, make way	427
Mary had a little baby	164
Matthew had been sitting	428
May the mind of Christ my Saviour	165
Maybe you can't draw or sing	429
Mighty in victory	430
Mighty is our God	431
Mister Noah built an ark	167
M-m-m-m-must I really go	426
Morning has broken	166
My faith is like a staff of oak	168
My God is so big	169
My Lord is higher than a mountain	170
New every morning	171
Noah was the only good man	432
Now be strong	172
Now Saul was rejected	433
Now thank we all our God	175
Now the day is over	173
Now the green blade riseth	174
O come, all you faithful	176
O come, O come, Emmanuel	177
O give thanks to the Lord	434
O happy day	178
O little town of Bethlehem	182
O Lord my God!	179
O Lord, You're great	435
O! O! O! how good is the Lord	180
O sinner man	194
O the love that drew salvation's plan	181
O when the saints go marching in	195
Oh, how He loves you and me	436
Oh no! The wine's all gone	437
Oh, oh, oh, oh	438
Oh, the Lord looked down	184
Oh, yes I am	439
Old man Noah	440
On Calvary's tree	183
On Christmas night	441
On Jordan's bank the Baptist's cry	186
On the road to Damascus	442
Once in royal David's city	185
Once there was a house	444
Once upon a time	443
One and two and three and four	445
One day when heaven	187
One more step along the world I go	188
One, two, three, Jesus loves me	189
Only a boy called David	190
Our eyes have seen the glory	191
Our Father who is in heaven	192
Our God reigns	84
Our harvest day is over	193
Peace I give to you	196
Peter and James and John	197
Peter and John	198
Praise and thanksgiving	447

Praise God, from whom all blessings flow 199
Praise Him 446
Praise Him on the trumpet 200
Praise Him, praise Him 203
Praise Him, praise Him, all you little children 201
Praise Him, praise Him, praise Him in the morning 202
Praise, my soul, the King of heaven 204
Praise to the Lord our God 205
Prayer is like a telephone 448
Put your hand in the hand 206

Rejoice in the Lord always 208
Remember all the people 207
Ride on, ride on 209
Rise and shine 210
Roll the stone 449

Said Judas to Mary 211
Saul had made himself 450
Saviour of the world 216
Search me, O God 212
See, amid the winter snow 213
See Him lying on a bed of straw 214
See the man walking 451
See, to us a Child is born 452
Seek ye first 215
Shalom, my friend 217
Shine bright 453
Silent night 219
Silver and gold have I none 198
Sing a new song to the Lord 454
Sing and celebrate (Christmas) 456
Sing and celebrate (Easter) 457
Sing praise 455
Sing we the King 218
Six hundred years old 458
So we're marching along 459
Some people laugh 462
Someone's brought a loaf of bread 220
Sometimes I'm naughty 460
Sometimes problems 461
Soon and very soon 221
Sorry, Lord 463
Spies were sent out 464
Spirit of God 465
Spirit of the living God 222
Stand up and bless the Lord 224
Stand up, clap hands 225
Stand up! stand up for Jesus 226
Standing in Your presence, Lord 466
Surely goodness and mercy 223

Tell me the old, old story 227
Tell me the stories of Jesus 228
Tell out, my soul 229
Thank You 230
Thank You for the love 467

Thank You, God, for sending Jesus 233
Thank You, Jesus 235
Thank You, Lord, for this fine day 232
Thank You, thank You, Jesus 231
The best book to read 234
The day You gave us 236
The fields are white 237
The first nowell 238
The greatest thing 239
The journey of life 468
The joy of the Lord is my strength 240
The King of love 241
The Lord has need of me 242
The Lord is my shepherd 244
The Lord is risen today 469
The Lord's my shepherd 243
The most important thing 470
The shepherds found 471
The Spirit lives 472
The steadfast love 250
The virgin Mary had a baby boy 251
The wise man built his house upon the rock 252
The wise may bring 253
The word of God 474
The word of the Lord is planted 473
There are hundreds of sparrows 246
There he stood - Goliath 475
There is a green hill 245
There is no-one else 476
There once was a man 477
There's a song for all the children 478
There's a song of exaltation 247
There's a way back 248
There's new life in Jesus 249
Think big: an elephant 479
Think of a world without any flowers 254
This Child 480
This is a catchy songa 481
This is the day 255
This joyful Eastertide 256
This little light of mine 258
Though the world has forsaken God 257
To God be the glory! 259
Turn your eyes upon Jesus 260
Twelve men went to spy 261
Two little eyes 262

Unto us a boy is born! 263

Wandering like lost sheep 482
We are soldiers of the King 483
We have a king who rides a donkey 264
We have heard a joyful sound 266
We love to praise You 265

We need to grow 484
We plough the fields and scatter 267
We really want to thank You, Lord 268
We shall overcome 270
We three kings 271
We will praise 485
We'll praise Him on the trumpet 486
We're following Jesus 487
We've a story to tell 272
Were you there? 269
What a friend we have in Jesus 273
What a mighty God we serve 491
What a wonderful Saviour 274
What colours God has made 488
What do you give 489
What drives the stars 490
What made a difference 492
When God breathes 497
When I needed a neighbour 275
When I survey 277
When I'm feeling lonely 493
When Israel was in Egypt's land 276
When morning gilds the skies 278
When the dark clouds 494
When the Lord in glory comes 280
When the road is rough and steep 279
When the trumpet of the Lord 281
When we look up 495
When you're feeling good 496
Wherever I am 282
Wherever I am I will praise You 283
Whether you're one 284
While shepherds watched 285
Who is on the Lord's side 286
Who put the colours in the rainbow 287
Who took fish and bread 288
Who's the king of the jungle? 289
Wide, wide as the ocean 290
Will your anchor hold 291
With Jesus in the boat 292
Would you walk by 498

Yes, God is good 293
Yesterday, today, for ever 294
Yet to all who received Him 499
You are holy 500
You are the King of glory 295
You can weigh an elephant's auntie 501
You can't catch a plane 502
You can't stop rain from falling down 296
You're my maker 503
Your hand, O God, has guided 297
Your ways are higher than mine 298
Yours be the glory 299

Zacchaeus was a very little man 300